SEIZE TH[...]

The Autobiogr[...]

HELEN SHARMAN
and
CHRISTOPHER PRIEST

CASSELL PLC

VICTOR GOLLANCZ

LONDON

To Les

First published in Great Britain 1993
by Victor Gollancz

First Gollancz Paperback edition published 1994
by Victor Gollancz
A Division of the Cassell group
Villiers House, 41/47 Strand, London WC2N 5JE

© Helen Sharman and Christopher Priest 1993

The right of Helen Sharman and Christopher Priest
to be identified as authors of this work has been
asserted by them in accordance with the Copyright,
Designs and Patents Act, 1988.

A catalogue record for this book is
available from the British Library.

ISBN 0 575 05819 6

Printed and bound in Great Britain
by Cox & Wyman Ltd, Reading, Berks

Contents

Acknowledgements   7

List of Photographs   9

Foreword by Arthur C. Clarke   11

1   *8 Minutes and 50 Seconds:* The Launch   17

2   *26 Years:* One Small Life   44

3   *2 Days:* Soyuz   52

4   *13,000 to 4:* Selection Process   69

5   *6 Days of World Peace:* Mir – Home, Sweet Home   98

6   *4 to 2:* Selection for Training   109

7   *364 Kilometres and 51.6°:* Looking Back on Earth   130

8   *3 Days and 3 Hours:* Preparing for Russia   137

9   *12 Experiments, 125,000 Seeds and Some Snails:* Work in Space   145

10   *18 Months:* Training   151

11   *25 Minutes:* Landing   169

Epilogue   183

Index   185

Acknowledgements

Tim, for help, support and friendship.

Clive and Gordon, for keeping everything in check and understanding so much.

Mum and Dad, for being dropped in it by a daughter and dealing with everything so well.

Kevin, for a happy summer and so much more.

John Glover, Moscow Narodny Bank, for making the Mission possible.

Peter Howard, for keeping with us.

Everyone at the British Embassy in Moscow for making life easier.

Everyone living in my block of flats, for keeping 'mum'.

Robert Swan, for help and encouragement.

Chris, Les, Nigel and Pete, for keeping me sane, and the curries!

Penny and Tony, for help in forgetting the hassles.

Philippa, for all the time together.

Clare, for friendship.

GBJUNO Schools, for perseverance and interest.

Peter Horncastle, for providing information about the psychological tests for this book.

Tony, for guidance along new paths.

Lord Dainton, for advice and being 'an uncle'.

Don Hardy, Serco, for introducing me to Serco Space.

Allan Johnson and Jerry Wellington, University of Sheffield, for detailed care and help with educational matters.

Bob Eagle, Mars Confectionery, for smoothing the way and taking it seriously!

Colin Flint, Birkbeck College, for patience with possibly the longest time on record to complete a Ph.D.

Ron Kennett, Royal Aeronautical Society, for continuing help and support.

List of Illustrations

Following page 48

Andrea, Mum, Berry the dog and Helen, summer 1970

Gordon Brooks, Clive Smith, Helen and Timothy Mace, outside the Science Museum before going to Russia

Helen and Tim outside the Cultural Centre in Star City

Gagarin's statue in front of Helen's block of flats

Ryoko Kikuchi, Valentin Alexeivich Gagarin, Toyohiro Akiyama, Clements Lothaller (Austria) and Helen on the anniversary of Gagarin's death

Star City

Helen undergoing the bicycle stress test

Yet another nasal examination

Sea training in the event of a splash landing

Tim and Helen before a simulated training exercise

Weightless training

The Soyuz Rocket

Suiting up on launch day

Waving goodbye on the steps up to the gantry: Sergei, Helen and Tolya

First view of Earth from space

Tolya and Sergei in the command module after jettisoning the final rocket stage

Our first dinner table on Soyuz

Following page 144

Space Station Mir

The module and Earth

Helen with biological experiments on Mir

Musa, Sergei and Viktor in the base block

Helen's bedroom

Helen in her sleeping bag

The view from Mir: Salt Lake; a crossroads in the Northern
    American States; Western England, Wales and Ireland from
    space; Cape Cod

Dusk . . . and sunrise

Musa, Sergei, Helen and Viktor calling Mission Control

The rescue team arrives

Home at last

Walking to the helicopter

Foreword

In 1993, the British Interplanetary Society celebrated the sixtieth year of its founding by a young Liverpool engineer, P. E. Cleator. As most of today's Britons were born *after* the launch of the first Earth satellite, Sputnik 1, in 1957, they will find it quite impossible to imagine the general attitude towards space travel in those far-off days. The expression 'Crying for the Moon' epitomized everything that was utterly unobtainable; and as late as 1956, no less a person than the Astronomer Royal declared: 'Space travel is utter bilge.' I am happy to say that he lived to see the Moon landing, and the total revolution of his science by space technology.

Yet it was great fun, back in those days, being members of an eccentric and often ridiculed minority (the BIS membership barely reached three figures before the war). Though we seldom convinced our critics, we could never be defeated in argument because – as history proved – we knew our facts and the opposition didn't. ('How can rockets work in a vacuum, where there's nothing to push against?' etc., etc.)

Although we were quite certain that spaceflight was inevitable, I doubt if even the most optimistic of us imagined that it would happen in our lifetimes. And we were indeed optimistic, hopelessly underestimating the cost and difficulty of achieving in practice what seemed straightforward on paper. It is with some embarrassment that I recall writing a propaganda leaflet – I hope that no copies have survived – claiming that a trip to the Moon need cost no more than one of the Royal Navy's destroyers. Even allowing for inflation, that was about a thousand times too low.

Thirty years ago, in the early dawn of the Space Age, I paid an affectionate tribute to my colleagues in the British Interplanetary Society with an essay entitled 'Memoirs of an Armchair Astronaut (Retired)'. So it is with great satisfaction that I introduce Britain's first *non*-armchair astronaut, Helen Sharman, who I had the pleasure of meeting on my last visit to the UK in 1992. Her account of the hours before launch and the actual sensations during ascent to orbit is so gripping that any reader will feel a vicarious involvement. This is exactly what it *must* be like. I can also confirm that her portrait of the generous and mischievous Cosmonaut Leonov is right on target. When Alexei's up to his tricks, it's not easy to remember what courage it must have taken to be the very first man to step outside a spacecraft and float in the empty void.

Although no one can deny that satellites have transformed our world through their applications in meteorology, communications, position finding, resource management – and, not least, peace-keeping – there are still many sceptics who question the value of sending human beings into space. Some of this scepticism may be due to the discovery that the Universe is a much tougher and more hostile place than we imagined, and not at all like that depicted in the endless re-runs of *Star Trek*. True, the Moon turned out to be exactly as predicted, but we had great hopes for Mars and Venus before the Mariners and Vikings demolished them.

In addition, the urgent social and economic problems of Planet Earth have made attempts to explore our neighbouring worlds seem like escapist fantasies. But we need dreams and when an organism ceases to explore its environment, it is beginning to die. Long after the troubles of our time are forgotten, history will still remember that this was the century in which mankind became a space-faring species.

Almost fifty years ago, in *Prelude to Space*, I made an attempt at self-fulfilling prophecy by proclaiming: 'We will take no frontiers into Space.' I am happy to say that this hope has been fulfilled and indeed is enshrined in United Nations declarations. Interplanetary imperialism seems an unlikely prospect.

But national pride is a different matter, as long as it is free from arrogance or hostility towards other sub-divisions of the human family. One of the most charming features of *Seize the Moment* is its portrayal of friendships which transcended accidents of birth and upbringing. Even during the height of the unlamented Cold War, astronauts and cosmonauts were able to maintain sincere personal friendships, sometimes despite the wishes of their superiors.

We British may have played only a minor rôle in manned – er, personned – space exploration, but we have made massive contributions to its achievement. (Did not one of the Apollo astronauts, on his way home, remark that 'Sir Isaac Newton is doing the driving now'?) So I have no reservations in congratulating Helen Sharman on being the first Briton into space.

And who, I wonder, will be the first on the Moon . . . ?

. . . and on Mars . . . ?

ARTHUR C. CLARKE
Commander of the British Empire
Chancellor, International Space University

SEIZE THE MOMENT

1

The Launch

18 May 1991

The doctor came to wake me at six that morning, but I was already awake, lying in the half-light of dawn. I had hardly slept at all. Although we were supposed to have been in bed by nine o'clock the previous evening it was after two-thirty in the morning when we finally crept to our rooms.

I was in what our Soviet hosts called the cosmonauts' 'hotel': a low, modern building subtly screened from the outside world by a number of *karagach* elms planted around the perimeter. The outside world, or that part of it closest to the hotel, was the science city of Leninsk, deep in Kazakhstan, about 150 kilometres to the east of the Aral Sea. Other than arriving from Moscow at the local airport I had seen almost nothing of Leninsk, because we had been in 'quarantine' (forced seclusion before the launch) ever since our arrival. In any event, the focus of all my interest and attention was the vast area of desolate scrubland a few kilometres to the north of the town, known throughout the world as the Baikonur Cosmodrome.

Here, already mounted on its launch pad, stood the rocket which later that day would carry Soyuz TM–12 on its mission to the Mir* space station. I had been training for eighteen months for my chance to be aboard that mission.

* In Russian the word 'mir' means both 'world' and 'peace'.

While my doctor* carried out the routine tests on heart-rate, breathing and blood pressure I was aware of noises and movement in and around the hotel compound. TV crews and journalists had been in position since the week before, numerous military and civilian dignitaries had flown in from different parts of the Soviet Union and of course diverse teams of medical advisers and scientific and engineering trainers had been here all along.

The examination was methodical and careful, but at this late stage it was only a last-minute precaution, and as soon as the doctor left I showered and dressed, then went to breakfast. I am always a little surprised by the interest people seem to have in this last meal before a launch. They are presumably thinking of condemned men and hearty breakfasts, but for me and all the people with whom I had been training over the months it was just the last chance we had to relax together. In addition to the two cosmonauts with whom I was going to fly, Sergei† the flight engineer and Tolya‡ my flight commander, there were several cosmonauts from earlier missions, including Leonov,§ the first man to walk in space, and Tim Mace, the British army officer with whom I had been training in the Soviet Union and who was now my back-up for the mission. Russian food was always something of a problem for me. I had been a vegetarian before I was selected for the Soviet space program, but to put it bluntly you would probably die of malnutrition in Russia if you tried to

---

* Dr Vladimir Krivalapov. Although the health of the cosmonauts is the concern of all the medical team in Star City, each member of the crew is allocated his or her personal physician.

† Sergei Konstantinovich Krikalyev, a civilian cosmonaut from Russia, married with a (then) baby daughter. Sergei had already been to the space station once before. He is cool, clever and has a good sense of humour.

‡ Anatole Pavlovich Artsebarski, from Ukraine, married with a (then) twelve-year-old son. This was Tolya's first launch, and he remained on Mir until October 1991. He's a good organizer, pays attention to detail, and has great stamina – he's always one of the last to leave a party.

§ Alexei Arkhipovich Leonov.

exist without meat. They give you meat at every meal and always with masses of butter and sour cream. Some of the food is delicious, but you also know it's the kind of stuff that is not doing you much good. When I first went to the Soviet Union I took a supply of pulses and nuts, so if I couldn't face one meal or another I could just miss it out and get the right sort of protein when I was by myself, and whenever I had had a chance to take a short trip to the West I always made sure I brought back more supplies. In this respect, the day of the launch was like all the others: breakfast was my own concoction of muesli and UHT milk.

I had packed up most of my stuff the night before, but after breakfast I went straight back to my room for one last look around. They had given me a tiny suite to myself: a living room, a bedroom and a bathroom. In traditional Russian style the bathroom was a bit spartan. No plugs in the bath or hand-basin, of course, although I had been tipped off about that in Britain and taken some plugs of my own. The problem was more that you did not want to use the bath at all, because it was so grotty. I preferred to shower, although getting hot water at the right time of day was next to impossible. (It was hot for about one hour a day, just before the time we played sport; by the time we got back to the hotel it was cold again.) The rest of the suite was furnished in a way that over the last year and a half had come to be familiar to me: there were carpets, net curtains, heavy main curtains, a colour TV, a fridge. (The Russians are obsessed with fridges: you find them everywhere you go. Even our classroom in Star City had a fridge.) None of these things is in any way exceptional to someone from the West, but the sheer monotony of seeing the same arrangement in every room I stayed in had made me feel they were in some way typical of Russian style. The fact that we were now in Kazakhstan only seemed to underline the uniformity of Soviet thinking and planning.

I had been back in my room for a few minutes when one of the young women from the medical staff came to give me the alcohol rub-down. This is the final bodily sterilization before dressing for the flight. As soon as it was finished I got dressed again, this time putting on over my own underwear the comfortable sterile underclothes for the mission: a full-sleeved T-shirt and long johns, both made out of white cotton. On top of these I put on my one-piece training suit.

It was at this point that one of the most extraordinary days of my life really began, a day of physical exertion and mental exhilaration, immense velocities, incomparable altitudes and encounters with odd and often bemusing traditions.

The first of these traditions was observed as I left my room. Soviet cosmonauts traditionally sign their names on the back of their room doors on the day they fly, a custom, like so many in the Soviet space program, that had begun with Yuri Gagarin. My name happened to be the first written on the door of that particular room, but down the corridor, where I rejoined Tolya and Sergei, we all inscribed our names on their door, a little self-consciously, in the lights from the TV crews.

One of the features of life in the Soviet Union I had started to get used to was the paradox of the chaotic but leisurely way events were organized. There always seemed to be plenty of time, no matter how complex things were getting. So it was on this morning. We were all gradually herded out of the hotel into the warm air of mid-morning. Although the cosmodrome is at a latitude further north than Chicago, it is a semi-desert region with hot, arid summers and cold winters. At the time of my flight, which was at the end of May, the weather was pleasantly warm and breezy during the days. We walked along a little path between the elms, feeling the warmth building around us, and down into the large car park. Here our convoy of buses, press vehicles and police cars awaited us.

The cheerful chaos continued even after we had boarded the bus. All sorts of things were happening in a very Russian sort of way. People were pestering us with one thing and another. For instance they put on some videos for us to watch while we were on the bus, intended to be a big surprise for the two cosmonauts in my crew. Their wives and families had been filmed and were being pressed by an invisible interviewer for farewell messages. While this was going on one person after another came up and talked to us over the noise. One of the earlier cosmonauts who was also a doctor came up and started giving me last-minute advice. 'Once you get weightless, and your body-fluids start to move up,' he said, 'make sure you're wearing the braslets around the tops of your legs'. I had heard this a dozen times and he must have known that, but I knew he was probably nervous on my account, so I promised him I would not forget these ties. Then one of the engineers came up and said, 'If the rocket sounds as if it's vibrating a bit on the way up, we're trying out a new kind of fuel.' I couldn't tell whether he was joking or not; perhaps it was the kind of thing they told the rookie cosmonaut, like sending the apprentice out on his first day to buy striped paint. Meanwhile, the video was playing loudly at the front, the other cosmonauts' families being clumsily interviewed: 'Do you have a message for your husband?' and other inspiring questions. I felt embarrassed for them. Tolya's wife Natasha, whom I had met several times, was clearly moved by the whole thing, knowing that she was unlikely to see her husband again for another five months. She was struggling against tears. The best she could come up with was banal sentiments like, 'I wish you all the best.' My own wish was to have the guts to rush up the bus and turn it off, because I knew Tolya and Sergei well enough to realize that they too would be embarrassed by the whole thing.

Through the bus's windows I could see we were moving slowly away from the outskirts of Leninsk and into the scrubland beyond. In front of us was a cavalcade of police cars, their lights flashing, and on each side of us the local people were lining the streets to see us go by. I began to realize how the long months of training had desensitized me to the sheer impact space travel had on other people. The intensive, repetitive and sometimes arduous training had deliberately drummed out all the excitement, so that when you came to do the job you could concentrate on it. To the crowds outside, to the visitors who had come from all over the world to witness the launch, to the unseen thousands and millions who watched on TV, we were the latest crew of cosmonauts and we were heading for outer space.

Yes, it was a special feeling, but it was one of the few times I had felt it since joining the Juno mission. As soon as you arrive in Star City and meet the other cosmonauts you realize that to them it's just a job, one that some of them have been doing for twenty years. An unusual job, perhaps even a dangerous job, but still, once you throw yourself into it, just a job that you're being paid to do. Even when people came up and asked for my autograph, as sometimes they did, I felt a certain sense of unreality, realizing that it was based on a perception of what I was doing, rather than the reality of it. Yet sitting on that slow-moving bus, heading for the launch site, I knew it was one of the few occasions when the two coincided. This was what I had trained for all those months actually to do and it was what people wanted to see, what enthralled them.

Finally we reached the MIK assembly area, a vast complex of factories and laboratories where the Soviet space vehicles were actually made and assembled. The cosmonauts' section is a small and fairly insignificant part of it and we had been out here many times in the past. This was where we had been able to see our capsule for the first time, practise getting into and out of it and make sure that everything inside was as we wanted it to be.

Today, though, the place seemed to be swarming with people, with more arriving all the time. Our convoy stopped near the cosmonauts' entrance and gradually the crew and the rest of the entourage got down from the bus and walked inside. As we passed through, what I noticed most was that everyone was wearing face-masks . . . for our protection, not theirs. (The whole idea of what the Russians called quarantine was to keep us away from minor infections; the last thing you want in a weightless space station is someone coughing at you! Anyway, falling ill in space could present a threat to the whole mission.) Behind their masks everyone looked excited and friendly, waving to us as if they had never seen us before.

Again came the feeling of unhurried chaos. We were here to put on our spacesuits, but it was all done in leisurely stages. After we had changed into fresh underclothes the doctors fitted us with the chest belt that we each had to wear throughout the launch: this contained an electrocardiograph to measure our heartbeat and rate and depth of breathing. Then on top of this we put back our training suits, and went along for another meal. After this, at last, came the spacesuits proper.

Russian spacesuits are of a relatively simple design, with two layers. The inner layer, made of a tough but rubbery material, is the airtight one; the outer layer, another tough artificial fabric, acts as protection for this, but also contains pockets, flaps, zippers and so on, for practical use. The suit opens at the front, where the stomach is, and you clamber in, sliding your legs in first. It's easier if the staff help you into it: they lift the back and chest part on to you, while you slip your arms in. The helmet goes on last, and when it's in place you seal up the hole through which you just climbed. This is called the appendix. Sealing it is fairly primitive: you ruffle up the material into a bunch, then use a rubber stretchy tie, rather like a strong elastic band, and tie it tightly around. You clip it together, then you do it a second time, to be sure. You push this inside the main body of the spacesuit, and close the two zips at the front. With the appendix bunched up inside the suit it's a bit like having a heavy book tucked under your coat . . . but of course the outer layer is designed to hold it.

When you first put on a spacesuit it feels heavy and stiff. Although this gets a little easier with time, in fact a spacesuit is one of the most unwieldy and inconvenient garments imaginable. The only time you feel at all comfortable inside it is when you are in the position for which it was designed to be used: lying in the capsule on your back with your knees up. Walking around is difficult because the suit is internally wired for strength, in case of catastrophic loss of atmosphere inside the capsule, and so you are constantly pushing against this restraint all the time you're trying to walk. Even so, you feel a certain practical attachment to the suit. It's fireproof, waterproof, airtight, ventilated. It's one of the ways which might help you survive should anything go wrong. So you're careful with your suit, perhaps even over-careful with it. You try not to bump into things when you're wearing it, or to snag it against sharp corners.

As soon as the staff had the spacesuits on us, they pumped us up to be sure we were airtight. The standard atmosphere of air pressure at ground level (1 atm.) is impractically high for use in spacesuits, because the combination of internal stiffeners and bulging limbs would make it virtually impossible to work. The Russians therefore use two pressure settings: 0.44 atm. above capsule pressure (which will keep you alive and fully able to function within the capsule, even if you would not be capable of much physical movement), and 0.27 atm. above ambient (keeps you alive for a shorter time, but allows easier movement). This pressure test on the ground therefore inflated us to 1.44 atm., while the staff made sure we were not leaking air anywhere, in particular that the helmet and gloves were properly sealed, and that we had tied the appendix properly. When this was finished, we manually tested the pressure-release valve on each suit (the large knob on the chest of the suit) to make sure we could reduce the pressure to 0.27 atm. When you're in a spacesuit you rely on outside air as much as possible, so that while still on Earth you keep the helmet open, and in the capsule you breathe the air in the cabin. In practice, the spacesuit and helmet are only sealed up during launch and re-entry, but the spacesuit remains your best hope of survival if there's some kind of accident with the craft.

We had been through pressure tests many times in training, but today the people around us seemed relaxed and casual and the three of us had plenty of time to chat to each other while it was going on. I felt again that at last we had come to the culmination of all those long months of training. We were actually getting ready to do something, not just training for it. It was the real thing. Logically, you would expect these last few hours on Earth to be tense, but I was simply glad to be getting on with it at last.

All three of our spacesuits pressurized correctly at the first attempt, which gave us more time to spare before the launch itself. We knew that a final press conference had been arranged, and indeed the spacesuit tests had been carried out in three seats facing the curtained glass wall behind which the world's press was assembling. As we waited for the curtains to be pulled back I felt a sudden worry about my family.

I had been expecting to see them all day. They were supposed to have been brought to the hotel in the morning, before we set out, and I had been promised that I would be able to have a private meeting with them. In fact, not only did they not turn up, none of the officials had seemed to know anything about where they might be. As we had gone from one stage to the next, I kept hoping they would suddenly appear. This press conference was just about the last remaining chance for me to see them. It came as quite a relief, then, that shortly before the curtains opened one of the staff whispered to me that the plane from Moscow had landed an hour or two late, but that everyone had now been brought over from the airport. Even so, it wasn't until the curtains were pulled open that I was sure I would see them.

All was well, however. Mum and Dad had been given seats in the first row, immediately in front of me. My sister Andrea was next to them, and my brother Richard was in the row behind. They were obviously as pleased to see me as I was to see them, but once the first rush of delight was out of the way it quickly dawned on all of us that this was going to be a far from private meeting. The only way we could communicate was through microphones, with everything, no matter how trivial or personal, instantly translated into Russian. At times of departure you feel as if there's everything and nothing to say, but in this press conference, no matter what it was, or how trivial, we heard it repeated and regurgitated around us. We put a cheerful face on it, but to be honest it was excruciating.

Meanwhile, looking superbly dignified under the circumstances, Tolya and Sergei sat beside me, more or less neglected by everyone. Only the three of us knew how unfair it was: all the attention was on me, but only because I was a Briton, the outsider, the novelty. What I wanted and what we had all expected, perhaps naïvely, was questions about the mission, or at least about British participation in the Soviet space program. But also, what I had hoped for was a few private moments with my family . . . not here, not through a glass screen under camera lights. While Tolya and Sergei sat by, one the commander of the mission and the other an experienced cosmonaut, my family and I made public small-talk.

Even so, I was glad to see them all!

At last the press conference straggled to its inane conclusion and with almost tangible relief we headed for the parade ground outside for the ceremonial send-off.

Three small white squares were painted on the tarmac and Tolya, Sergei and I walked across to them and took up our positions. Here, as in many small events, we followed a tradition set down by Gagarin on the momentous day of his launch.

From the centre box, Tolya saluted the marshal in charge of this part of the proceedings, General-Colonel Vladimir Ivanov, and said, 'My crew and I have been made ready and now we are reporting that we are ready to fly the Soyuz TM–12 mission.'

The general saluted back.

He said, 'I give you permission to fly. I wish you a successful flight,' and then added, with a wry smile, 'and a soft landing.'

Once again I felt I was the rookie, not quite in on all the nuances, but it was a friendly little ceremony and as soon as it finished and we turned towards our waiting bus, a great cheer went up from all the onlookers. My father and brother were there in the crowd close to the bus, although at that moment I couldn't see Mum or Andrea.

As we headed for the bus steps, Leonov stepped forward. He was grinning at us with obvious mischievous intent, but I couldn't quite see what he was up to. I was just about to ask Tolya what was going on, when I saw that Mum had managed to get right round to the door of the bus. At last we were able to steal a quick hug! Tolya and Sergei were beside us, climbing aboard. Leonov, still grinning, delivered to each of them a hearty whack on the backside. As I disentangled myself from Mum and clambered clumsily up the steps, he walloped my backside too.

Our long blue and silver bus edged slowly away from the parade ground and began the journey towards the launch site. I was craning my neck in the uncomfortable spacesuit helmet mounting, trying to catch a last glimpse of Mum and Dad, but also glancing forward in the direction the bus was heading, knowing that the Soyuz rocket must soon come into sight. I was touched to realize how important Gagarin and his fabulous flight remained to the modern-day cosmonauts. His statue was in the grounds outside my apartment in Star City and another stood on an immense pillar in an important Moscow street called Leninski Prospekt, and from my first days in Russia I had learned to revere and cherish this courageous man's memory, just as all the other cosmonauts did. One of my most moving experiences in the Soviet Union had been when Tim Mace and I were taken to the place where Gagarin died. The site where the MiG–15 he was flying had crashed is now a shrine, with another memorial and a tablet recording his life and that of the instructor who died with

him. Every spring, the people who look after this shrine trim the
tops of the trees along the angle of the crashing plane, so that it is
possible to stand by his memorial and look up and see the gap to
the sky. It sounds gruesome, but when you are there all you
think about is how much the Russians still love the man. He was
the first cosmonaut Hero of the Soviet Union and, as I was
discovering, his innocent actions, mighty and trivial, still
haunted the present. Not only the speeches; the film they had put
on for us the night before, *White Sun in the Desert*, was the one he
had watched the evening before his flight. There were more
Gagarin memorabilia to come!

A short distance from the rocket assembly building the Soyuz
rocket came into view. Some of the men inside the bus were
standing in the aisle, looking back the way we had come, peering
towards each side of the bus. Then Leonov shouted, 'OK!' and
the bus came to a complete halt.

Sergei and Tolya grinned and moved towards the door of the
bus. I looked quizzically at Leonov, who was standing beside
my seat.

'Gagarin stopped here,' he said, as if that explained everything.

I stood up, thinking that he meant I should climb out of the
bus with the others.

'Tradition,' said Leonov. 'But you don't have to worry about
it this time . . . unless you really need to, of course!'

With a jolt I realized what was going on. This was one
tradition they would not expect me to join in. What was a
relatively straightforward procedure for a man would involve
me in completely removing my spacesuit.

'It's OK, Ilenechka,' Leonov said, using the Russian diminu-
tive of my name. 'But while they are busy we have something
else to do . . .'

Leonov signalled to the mission's 'methodist' (meaning, in
effect, the man who had worked through the 'methods', or
training procedures, with us). The methodist had brought with

him a lot of stuff we had given him the night before. These were
personal items we wanted semi-officially to take on the rocket.
For instance, there were my camera and several rolls of film,
earplugs . . . and my Swiss Army knife. Knives are not allowed
in the space station, in case of accidents, but Tolya had seen me
with my knife a few days before and suggested I might smuggle
it aboard. Knives are useful things to have around when you
have to do a lot of general maintenance work. Something else I
had asked the methodist to keep for me was the 'start key'. This
was my only nod towards what Russians called tradition and
what I thought of as superstition: the start key had been used to
switch on the electronic control systems for one of the earlier
launches. I had seen it on display in one of the museums we had
been round during our two weeks in quarantine and they had
said I could carry it for luck.

I pushed all this stuff into the pockets of my spacesuit, with
Leonov standing beside my seat. He was still keeping an eye on
the other two, awkwardly maintaining the Gagarin legend
against the side of the bus.

He gave me a little handful of grass, and said, 'I picked this for
you. Take it with you into the space station. There's nothing
much to smell up there and this will remind you of home.'

I took the grass and rubbed it lightly between my fingers. It
gave off a pleasant, sweet herbal aroma.*

'And something else.' Leonov reached into the pocket inside
his jacket. 'The first night you're on the space station, it's
traditional for all the crew to eat a proper dinner together. Those
two guys already up there won't have had a proper meal,
especially with a lady, for six months. I thought you might like
to dress for dinner.'

'What do you mean?'

'I went into Leninsk the other day and bought you something.'

---

* I later found out that this fragrant plant called *polin*, which grows all over
the Kazakh steppes, was a kind of wormwood, or absinthe.

Grinning all over his face he produced a small bundle of pink fabric, which on unfolding turned out to be a kind of all-in-one jumpsuit made out of chiffon, with elasticated bits to go round my knees and a wonderful frilly front and billowing sleeves.

'I got one of the ladies at the hotel to make it up for you,' Leonov said. 'Just for fun.'

Outside the window I could see the two helmeted heads of Sergei and Tolya moving back towards the steps of the bus, so I quickly undid the zips of the spacesuit and pushed the frilly garment inside the chest piece. Still smiling to himself, Leonov went back to his seat.

While the bus resumed its slow journey, the methodist gave Sergei and Tolya their own bits and pieces they wanted to smuggle aboard. They sat down in their seats and looked across at me as if to make sure I was still there. I acknowledged them, feeling suddenly serious and committed to the job ahead. Imperceptibly, the mood on the bus had changed, because with the fooling about behind us, we were now driving directly towards the launch pad, and the rocket was straight ahead.

It was the first time I had been able to get a good, uninterrupted look at it. Nothing in training can prepare you for the prospect of your own rocket, the real one, the actual one that is going to start its engines and lift you away from the Earth. There was ours. It was grey and solid against the neutral sky, the three main supporting gantries by now tipped back on their counterweights. All that remained were the four small launch-gantries clustered around the base and the tower with the elevator that would lift us to the capsule. White condensation poured off the rocket, seeming to roll down its flanks, a momentary slow-motion illusion of the upward rush for which it had been built. The rocket was a little smaller than perhaps I had expected, but there was something so purposeful, almost heroic, about its utilitarian lines that I could only stare at it in awe. I felt a tremendous sense of respect for it, as if it were, itself, alive.

Close to the top, on the white-painted fairing that surrounded the capsule inside which I would soon be seated, they had painted two flags: the Soviet flag and, for the first time in manned space travel, the Union Jack.

The bus came to a halt at the base of the rocket and the three of us climbed down first. Most of the people who had been with us stayed on the bus, staring out at us silently through the windows. On the pad some of the technicians waved and cheered. We walked the short distance to the metal steps, right against one of the huge booster rocket engines of the first stage. Tolya went first, I followed and Sergei was behind. We turned for the photographers, waved and smiled. We were there, by the rocket, looking back, no time to think of what it all meant, still creatures of the weird mechanisms of cosmonaut life, half of them the endless, arduous, torturous training for a seriously responsible job, the other half the temporary fame and glamour, the waving farewells and chattering cameras, the mindless interviews and press conferences. Now the last photographs, the last smiles.

Tolya turned first, and Sergei and I quickly followed. Behind us, at the top of the steps, was an elevator cage and the man inside was waiting to take us to the top. We clambered in, huge and ungainly in our padded suits. There was hardly room for Sergei, but he pressed in and the operator swung the gate closed behind him.

Below us, the bus was already moving away. A few of the technicians stared up at us. The elevator lurched and we began to rise slowly towards the top.

I watched the body of the rocket slip by beside me. It was covered in ice! Layers and layers of ice, moulded against the metal of the rocket, condensed out of the atmosphere against the bitterly cold fuel tanks. We rose steadily through the white mist of water vapour. I glanced behind: already we seemed to have risen high into the air, but when I tipped back my head to look upwards the bulk of the rocket still stretched above us. Now we were actually close against it, rising slowly up the side of the rocket, the sheer scale of it was daunting. From the bus it had for a moment seemed surprisingly small; now it towered magnificently over me, glinting with ice in the brilliant sunshine, leaking its cold white fumes, grey and dark and tall, built for space.

When the lift arrived at the top there was a small platform giving access to the hatch. The wind was blowing stiffly up here and I could feel the platform and rocket swaying to a significant degree. We were of course insulated from the weather by our suits, but as the technicians on the platform were working in shirtsleeves I imagine it was not unpleasant to be in.

After brief greetings all round, it was time to board the rocket. Sergei went in first; this was partly because he was in one of the two outer seats, and partly because as the engineer it was his job to make a final check of the command capsule. He would make sure that everything we had asked to be made ready was there for us, that the seats were bolted down correctly and so on. It didn't take him long and in a few moments I heard him say, 'OK, you can get in now.'

It was my turn next. The staff removed the anti-scratch protective cover from my helmet and I sat down on the lip of the hatch and hauled myself in head first. One of the technicians pulled off my outer boots and then I swung my legs inside.

Beneath me was an inner hatch, leading down to the command capsule itself. I lowered myself into this feet first, turned around, then wriggled over to the right-hand seat. Sergei had already started working through his checklist.

I was now in the crew area of the rocket, and this consisted of three main sections. At the top was the orbital capsule, an elongated sphere, which I had just passed through, and which could provide enough room for one person at a time to stretch out. This was where we would live for the two days after launch while moving to orbital rendezvous with the space station. The

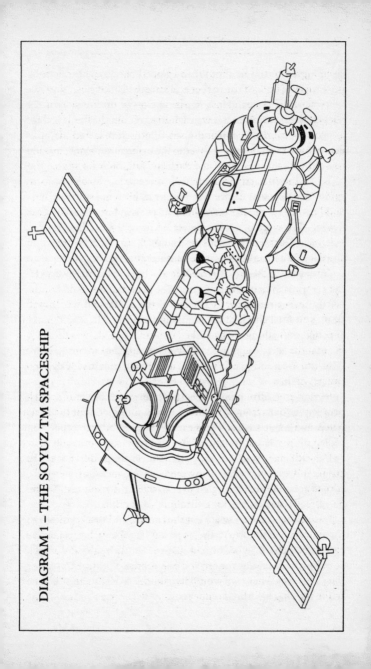

DIAGRAM 1 – THE SOYUZ TM SPACESHIP

command capsule was slightly larger but much more cramped. The main controls for the spacecraft were located here, together with our three seats. There were two small, circular sideways-facing windows, one beside each of the outer seats. (Nothing could be seen through the windows before the launch, because the orbital and command capsules were covered by the protective fairing, which would be jettisoned as soon as we were out of the Earth's atmosphere.) Much of the room inside the command capsule was taken up by equipment that would eventually be needed during the return to Earth: parachutes, flotation gear, emergency rations, survival gear, and so on. The third module of the crew section was one to which we had no access: it contained fuel tanks, oxygen and water supplies, and the mass of ancillary equipment that ran all the on-board systems. When the Soyuz finally returned to Earth, this third stage would be used as the main retro-rocket, before being jettisoned along with the orbital capsule. Only the command capsule, the re-entry capsule, actually landed.

As soon as I was in place Tolya followed, clambering down awkwardly in the confined space and taking the third seat, in the middle. There was not an inch of free space! We were all trying to ease ourselves down into the seats, bumping elbows and reaching across each other. We had to get the smuggled stuff out of our pockets and stowed safely in the capsule, because the spacesuits were designed so exactly to the shape of our bodies that any foreign objects could cause painful pressure points during the launch. Anyway, I wanted to keep Leonov's frilly garment out of their sight. This was my only secret from the others. When I thought Tolya and Sergei wouldn't notice what I was doing I slipped it out of the chest piece and quickly crammed it into the tiny space beneath my chair. Even so, Tolya saw the movement.

'What's that?' he said.

'Oh . . . just something else I brought along,' I said, trying to make it sound insignificant. Tolya nodded, lost interest and got back to what he was doing.

Our first act on the rocket was to close the inner hatch from below, then confirm to the bunker we had done so. Not long after we heard the outer hatch being closed by one of the technicians outside on the platform. There was a muffled thud, then a clang . . . and it was closed.

I glanced across at the other two and sensed in them the same feeling that had suddenly swept across me. The hatch is closed. It's over. There are no more doctors, no more lectures, no more press conferences, no more smiles and salutes and last-minute tips. The hatch is closed, sealing us away from the outside world, and we are here and it's about to begin.

The three of us set to work, paging through the long checklists, each of us preoccupied by our separate tasks.

This was probably the busiest time in the whole flight: we were not only working our way down the list of checks and doing it within a set period of time, but we were also having to talk to and fro with the bunker and keep listening to what the other two crew were talking about, alert for any problems that might arise, or changes in the launch plan. In addition we had to write down various measurements in the log book: for instance, we had to keep an eye on the air pressure not only in the command capsule but in the orbital capsule too. Condensation is also a problem when there are people inside a rocket. There were several valves that had to be opened and closed at certain times and we had a little hand-pump to move the condensate from one part to another.

It required total concentration, but was worse at some periods than at others. Some of the time there was a lot to be done in a few minutes and it was relentless: bang-bang-bang, do-it, do-it, do-it. When it was like this there was no way we could chat to each other. But then there would be short periods with nothing particular expected of us, maybe ten minutes at a time, and we would relax a bit and say a few things to each other. Even then we knew that every word we said was being relayed to the people on the ground, in the bunker, in mission control in Moscow . . . perhaps even to TV networks around the world. We could never be sure, so our conversation in the quiet patches tended to be about harmless physical matters. I remember, for instance, saying at one point that my feet were cold!

In fact my feet *were* cold. Thanks to a quirk of Russian spacesuit design, the ventilating air that was pumped in to keep us cool circulated best around the feet and did not seem to have much effect elsewhere. Overall I have never felt quite so hot at any other time in my life. Because of the weather, because of the physical exertions, our skin temperatures were quickly rising: a pool of warm perspiration began to collect in the small of my back, directly under me.

I was also discovering how little room I had on the right side of me, the one that was against the wall of the capsule. This was because of all the extra equipment and supplies they had shoved into the capsule that had not been there in the simulator. Tolya, against my left side, seemed to be all elbows; we were constantly bumping against each other when we moved to operate the equipment.

All through this period we were aware of continual movement and noise. The rocket was swaying perceptibly because of the wind outside and in addition we knew that all the ancillary equipment was being moved back before the launch could take place. Every now and then we would feel a shudder or vibration as something else was detached from the rocket. Each noise, each tremor through the body of the rocket, was a reminder of our isolation up there, high in the sky. In one of the quiet periods I suddenly remembered the ice crust on the main engine stage below me, the vapour rushing down towards the ground, the illusion of motion cloaking the unimaginable energy still dormant and pent up in the tanks and engines so far beneath us. That vast potential had become personal: it was there to lift *me* into space.

Immediately in front of our faces, dangling over our heads, was a little metal model of a spaceman, tied to the hatch by a piece of string. He was our talisman. All through these launch preparations the talisman swung to and fro as the rocket moved in the wind, a kind of insistent reminder of the physical world outside. It was not another good-luck charm (although it did remind me of the things people dangle inside their car windscreens), but actually had a function during the launch. Behind it was the on-board TV camera that monitored us and no matter which way the lens was turned the talisman could be seen swinging. It was a simple device for the people on the ground, who by watching its movements would be able to tell the exact moment in which we became weightless.*

Finally we got through the checklists and everything was confirmed to be in order, as right as it would ever be. Then at last we were able to rest. Not relax. I think that is a word whose meaning is lost on any astronaut in the last few minutes before a flight . . . but working inside hot spacesuits, in a cramped position, is physically arduous. We were tired and it was good to rest for a while. There were still about twenty-five minutes before lift-off. The methodist came on the radio and said, 'Would you like to listen to some music? What would you like to listen to?' Music is important to the Russians, it's a relaxation. So Sergei and Tolya said they would like some and we listened to some light Russian pop: this was probably more to the taste of the people in the bunker than to Tolya himself, who I knew preferred British rock.

We were in what the Americans call the final minutes of countdown, but the system is different in Russia. There is no countdown as such. The launch is timed to the clock and we

---

* To be strictly accurate, the word 'weightless' should always be printed in inverted commas when used to describe people or things floating around inside spacecraft. Most people know in general terms what 'weightlessness' is, but it is a state which, to be accurate, is unlikely ever to be achieved. See Chapter Nine.

knew the exact time at which various stages would pass, but there wasn't the constant reminder of the steadily ticking clock. Instead, the controller in the bunker would come on the radio at intervals and say, 'Twenty minutes to go,' or whatever it was. We would acknowledge this, but by this time there was hardly any traffic of conversation between us.

There was at last a little time to think.

Freshest in my mind was the press conference and as soon as I thought of it I squirmed briefly inside my spacesuit at the memory. Although none of it had been my fault, I none the less blamed myself for not realizing it was going to be like that and therefore for not being better prepared to deal with it. Thinking about the things I had said to my parents, I blamed myself partly for everything I had said and in equal measure for everything I had *not*. This last opportunity to speak to them frittered away in banalities! At the same time I remembered some of the things other people had said to me and these too were suddenly charged with dark significance: why had so-and-so said that and wasn't it said in an odd tone of voice? A psychologist might say that I was reacting unconsciously to the tension of these last minutes before lift-off (although if you had asked me I would have said I otherwise felt perfectly calm), but whatever the reason I felt full of belated regret and helpless to do anything about it.

In perhaps something of the same mood I started to think, for the first time ever, about similarities between me and the astronaut Christa McAuliffe, who died in the US Shuttle Challenger disaster. In recent months journalists had often asked me for my thoughts about the astronauts who had died in Challenger, presumably wondering how I felt about the prospect of being blown up. I had always shrugged off the questions, not out of bravado but because I genuinely believed the Soyuz flight was unlikely to be dangerous. And anyway, what on earth could I say, sensibly, about the prospect of being blown up in a spectacular launch explosion? However, lying there in those quiet moments before the launch began, thoughts about similarities between Christa McAuliffe and myself did go through my mind. For one thing we were both civilian women and in our different ways we had trained to be cosmonauts while surrounded by media attention. I knew many people in Britain would be watching this launch on TV, just as the Challenger launch had caught the attention of millions of ordinary Americans, and in particular we were both the focus of much interest from schoolchildren. She, like me, had sat there high inside a space vehicle, waiting for the torch to be lit beneath her. I thought, 'It couldn't happen twice, could it?' In that thought, of course, similarity died. Logic took over: she had had no precedent on which to dwell while the seconds ticked away and in any event the chances of my suffering an accidental death were neither raised nor lowered by hers. I wished I could have met and known her before she died, because we would probably have had a lot in common, but it would be pretentious and untrue to say I felt spiritually close to her.

I felt closer, spiritually and practically, with other people who had flown on Soyuz missions. For instance, one of the cosmonauts on the mission before mine had been a journalist from Japan called Toyohiro Akiyama. This was a purely commercial flight: the television station Toyohiro worked for had paid all the expenses in order to buy themselves an exclusive story. I had met Toyohiro in Star City and he told me that before starting the training he was completely unfit: he was a two-packs-a-day smoker and the heaviest thing he had ever lifted was a pen. He had gone through the training, though, those long months of physical and mental discipline, and at the end of it he emerged as a fully capable cosmonaut, fit as a fiddle, part of a professional team. Toyohiro had worked for and earned his place.

I had been down to Baikonur the previous December to watch Toyohiro's launch and it had made a profound impression on me. As I lay in my command capsule, waiting for the moment of launch to arrive, I felt I knew and understood a large part of what the people outside would be experiencing. The wait for ignition

seemed interminable out there, because there was little hint of
the activity inside the rocket and in the bunker. When the launch
finally began the sheer spectacle of the rocket rising into the sky
and the shattering noise that went with it were unforgettable.
Then the long minutes craning my neck, watching the ever-
diminishing flare of brilliant white light, the quickly vanishing
exhaust trail. When even this last trace could no longer be seen
everyone crammed around the TV monitors, because they were
the only things left for us to look at. At the end, when the rocket
was so far away even the TV link was lost, I gazed across the
scrubland at the launch site once more. The platform was less
than a mile away, empty now and silent, and I found that
spectacle inexpressibly moving. I had turned away, feeling
drained.

In my earphones, a voice from the bunker said, 'Five minutes to
go. Please close the masks of your helmets.'

The three of us obeyed, then confirmed. Our call-sign was
OZONE, and we identified ourselves by crew number. I was
the last to confirm, and so I said, 'OZONE 3, OZONE 3, my
helmet is shut. We are in the preparation régime, ready to go.'

The bunker replied, 'Understood, OZONE 3. We are also in
that régime. Everything on board is correct and we are now
ready to launch.'

A little later, the voice said, 'Two minutes.'

Then it said, 'One minute.'

Now that we were not moving around or reaching for the
controls above us, it was comfortable to be sitting there in
the spacesuit. I glanced at the little talisman, swinging from the
hatch above us. I felt the pressure of Tolya's elbow against mine.
I could hear the quiet hiss of static in the speaker against my ear.
Sergei said nothing, Tolya said nothing; the voice from the
bunker was silent. It was a moment of stillness, of final waiting.
My feet were still cold.

Far away, deep below, there came a rumbling noise as the rocket engines ignited. On the control panel the on-board clock had started automatically; we were nominally one second into the mission, then two, and the engines still rumbled far below. Three seconds, and the rumbling grew louder, and the four launch-gantries swung away. I could feel vibration but no sense of acceleration. I knew we must have left the ground and were in that momentary limbo where the rocket seems to balance precariously on its thrust, surely destined to topple. But the engines continued to roar beneath us and the instruments confirmed that we were away from the tower, that acceleration was beginning to build, and we could feel the pressure of g-forces growing steadily against us.

When I next looked at the clock we were twenty seconds into the flight and above us the talisman was taut on its string, no longer as free to swing. I could now sense the rocket's power not only from the vibrations coming through the seat but also from the increasing press of acceleration. The clock showed that forty seconds had elapsed. The voice from the bunker confirmed the successful launch and Sergei briefly responded. G-forces continued to grow; the rocket was getting lighter as the fuel burned away and we were picking up speed.

After 115 seconds came the first of several loud bumps and bangs: the escape rocket on the nose of the craft was being jettisoned. At this point we were 46 kilometres from the ground, on the threshold of space. Three seconds later there was another jolt, this one bigger and from below, as the first-stage booster rockets separated from us. This was the moment we passed the 50 kilometres mark, the height the Russians usually designate as the beginning of space.

Our smooth acceleration continued as the rocket grew lighter; now we were using the second-stage engine. This was the centrally mounted main engine, used from the moment of lift-off. It was still burning steadily when, 165 seconds into the flight, the protective fairing that covered the windows was jettisoned, no longer needed to protect the spacecraft from the atmosphere as there was little atmosphere left outside!

Sunlight streamed in. I looked down at the Earth. We were already over the Pacific!

Tolya said, 'What can you see? What can you see?' He had no window, and was dazzled by the golden sunlight pouring in.

I could see the curvature of the Earth! Speckly white clouds! A brilliant azure sea! The blackness of space! Now I knew I was where the theory told me I should be – out from the world, above the blue skies and diamond-studded clouds. Dreams sometimes do come true and I felt so alive!

The craft was rotating and the view turned away from me. Then it was Sergei's turn to see. Poor Tolya could only glimpse it.

Sergei said, 'It's snowing up here! The ice is breaking off!'

In the sunlight, in the vacuum outside my window, I too could see that chunks of ice were breaking away from the body of the rocket. If we had been in the atmosphere they would have been whipped out of our sight before we saw them, but here they spun away from the craft and we only left them behind because we were still accelerating.

The second stage separated after 288 seconds: another jolt, another bang sensed through the metal of the rocket, and for a brief moment our bodies felt lighter, almost as if they were about to drift out of our seats. I saw the talisman above me tremble, seeming to dither between floating and swinging, but then the third stage fired and tremendous acceleration immediately pressed us down again. The rocket had much less mass now and this final engine set about the last part of our launch in a fierce and energetic way. G-forces rose to a respectable $3\frac{1}{2}$g. The flight was at last thrilling me with the sensation of speed.

I glanced at the on-board clock. Five hundred seconds had elapsed since we lifted away from the pad. Just eight minutes ago I had been bound to the Earth's surface, now I was in space.

Eight minutes ago my family had been less than a mile away from me; now we were not even on the same planet.

At 530 seconds the third stage cut out and was jettisoned. It did not happen gradually. One moment it was burning ferociously behind me, in the next it stopped completely. One moment I was being pressed hard into my seat and in the next I was not. I had been straining against the g-force without realizing I had been doing so; then I stopped straining. Quite involuntarily, I said, '*Uhh!*'

Beside me, Sergei and Tolya said, '*Uhh!*'

The talisman was no longer tense against its string. It hovered by the hatch, the string snaking loosely towards it. It had suddenly become, as we had suddenly become, weightless.

2

One Small Life

Neither of my parents was an astronaut. No one else in my family had any discernible interest in astronautics: we have no astronomers, pilots, rocket designers or (beyond the usual sense of the word) dreamers. I did not plan to become an astronaut and most of my life before I went into space was spent without a single expectation that I ever would. Yuri Gagarin's flight took place in 1961, two years before I was born. When Aldrin and Armstrong landed on the Moon I was just six years old. The closest I ever came to showing an interest in space travel was once at junior school, when with all my friends in the class I constructed a crude model of a Saturn V rocket using silver milk-bottle tops (years later I ill-advisedly let word of this trivial event slip to a television programme director, and it has turned up in the tabloid press with depressing regularity ever since).

Space travel, it is clear, was not in the blood.

However, I did eventually go into space, it is now in my blood for good and my life will never again be the same.

I came into the world as Helen Patricia Sharman on 30 May 1963, in the Jessop Hospital for Women in the centre of Sheffield. There were no complications and after a few days my mother was sent home with me.

'There were no complications.' My early life is contained in that phrase. I grew up in an ordinary background that will be familiar to hundreds of thousands of British people of my age-group. Not, I know, a familiar background to everyone, but certainly to such a huge number of people that I feel a certain level of generalization is possible. My parents came originally from Boston, Lincolnshire. My father, John Sharman, is a college lecturer and administrator; my mother, Lyndis, was a nurse before I was born and now works as a nursing assistant at a cancer hospice in Sheffield. Although my parents have never been well off (and, indeed, were significantly hard up during the first years of their marriage), I was brought up in pleasant lower middle class suburbs, I went to ordinary state schools and ended my adolescence and full-time education with a degree from university.

My first home was a small semi-detached house in a cul-de-sac in Grenoside, now an outer suburb of Sheffield but in the early 1960s a village in the Sheffield outskirts on the way to Penistone.

My sister Andrea was born two years after me. We grew up together, forming as reasonably harmonious a twosome as sisters can; much later, when I was thirteen, my adopted brother Richard came along.

The first school I went to was Grenoside Junior and Infants, where I started when I was five. Here I embarked on a remarkably normal academic career by learning to read and write. I eventually learned to swim, to play the recorder, to ride a bike . . . and how to climb and fall out of trees. I became a determined and sometimes stubborn child, convinced that anything was possible so long as I persevered. 'I can do it,' is a phrase that I seem to have grown up with and that my parents suffered on many occasions. When I was eight my family moved to the southern suburb of Sheffield called Greenhill, and naturally enough I had to move to the local junior school.

I was a reasonably bright kid and had no real difficulty with any of the lessons. Looking at it all from the inside I saw nothing

special about myself or my abilities. I felt myself to be a part
of a process, one I happened to be good at but not in itself
a particularly special process. When I was eleven I went to
Jordanthorpe Comprehensive School, and stayed there until I
went to Sheffield University. From my early teens on I
remember that I was frequently impatient with the rituals and
routines of school. I disliked being treated like a child, being
made to hang around in wet playgrounds and so on, when I
would have been happier reading or doing something produc-
tive. I was never a rebel, though.

I left university in June 1984 with a 2:1 in Chemistry, and went
straight from there to my first job, with GEC. It was one of
several jobs I had applied for during my final year. I had no idea
what I wanted to do except that I enjoyed chemistry and wanted
to make use of my degree and, like most of the other people in
my year, I approached or was approached by the usual round of
big companies who recruit graduates with technical degrees.
Eventually I was offered seven jobs but, frankly, most people at
this stage, and I was certainly one of them, do not have the
experience to make a real decision about which would be the
most suitable. I selected GEC even though the salary on offer
was the lowest of all, because the work they were offering was
varied and the job would be based in London. By this time I
wanted to sample the 'bright lights' of the South-East.

I stayed at GEC for three years and I was happy there. My job
(engineer being the actual description) involved solving production problems, organizing some of the production schedules
and doing some research and development of the materials that
were used to go inside cathode ray tubes. The problem for me at
GEC was that after I had been there for two or three months, the
learning curve started to level off. When you are at university,
you feel as if you have learned something new every day. At first
it was like that at GEC; I was learning techniques and systems
and, inevitably, what industry was really about, the business of
making money. In particular, I was working with people of all

ages and from a wide variety of backgrounds. By the beginning of 1985 I was ready for more of a challenge, so when GEC said they would encourage me to work for a Ph.D., I enrolled at Birkbeck College in London, researching the luminescence of rare-earth ions in crystals and glasses.

My research at Birkbeck continued over the next few years, and I carried on with it after I moved to Mars Confectionery in August 1987, although now it was not directly or indirectly germane to my job and day release was no longer possible. I had become a research technologist in the New Products Division, working on an ice-cream product then in the planning stage.

I had three different jobs at Mars, ending up in the chocolate section of the R&D department. I found the transition from one company to another fascinating. At GEC the products on which I worked were few in quantity and high in price. At Mars each individual product had a price of only a few pence, yet literally tonnes were produced each day. The manufacturing processes were totally different, too. Mars had a lot of high-tech automated equipment, compared to more labour-intensive work in my department of GEC, though the final products were quite the reverse, with a good deal of electronic hardware and new equipment being incorporated into a cathode ray tube. Both jobs, however, involved work in a factory, using my hands and mental skills together (I always hated report-writing and desk work) and, what I enjoyed most of all, working with lots of different people.

The beauty of having a job as a scientist, especially in a manufacturing environment, is that you are able to incorporate so many facets of life into each working day. For instance, it's no good understanding and manipulating the chemistry of emulsifiers (the components that bind fat and water and stop them separating) in your ice-cream if the toffee falls off the ice-cream before its had a chance to harden, or if the poor person on the fork-lift doesn't have enough time to bring more wrappers to the production line before there's a pile-up of melting confectionery!

Mars had a completely different management structure and style from that of GEC. I loved it. The period at Mars was a turning point for me, in that I suddenly felt in control of my own life.

People who found their early years hard often have an interesting story to tell in later life: film stars, great artists, successful politicians and so on frequently look back to their childhood with a *frisson* of pleasurable horror, recalling injustice, privation, bullying, parental cruelty, living through domestic and national upheavals and the like.

This horrible pleasure is denied to me. My family background was stable and secure from the day I was born until the day I left home to go to university. There were family arguments, of course, but we stayed together, we grew together, no one beat up anyone else, no one became an alcoholic or a drug addict, no one close to me died in traumatic circumstances. My father had a steady job; my mother stayed at home to bring up her three children. We took holidays together, visited relatives at Christmas and no one ran away from home. Even now, although I am an adult and living two hundred miles from the place I still think of as home, our family remains stable.

At school I was not bullied, nor was I myself a bully. I won no coveted scholarships; equally, I was never punished for laziness or forced to take remedial classes. Although I was good at sports, I broke no school athletic records that I can remember, and if I did then I am certain they would have been re-broken soon afterwards. I had friends and no doubt I had some feudal contacts too.

In every street in every British town and village you will find someone like me.

Andrea, Mum, Berry the dog and Helen, cooling off
in Malham Tarn, summer 1970

Above Gordon Brooks, Clive Smith, Helen and Timothy Mace, outside the Science Museum before the announcement that Helen and Tim were going to Russia (the same day)   *Below left* Helen and Tim outside the Cultural Centre in Star City   *Below right* Gagarin's statue in front of Helen's block of flats

Above Ryoko Kikuchi, Valentin Alexeivich Gagarin, Toyohiro Akiyama, Clements Lothaller (Austria) and Helen on the anniversary of Gagarin's death at the place where his aircraft crashed

Below Star City from Helen's kitchen window

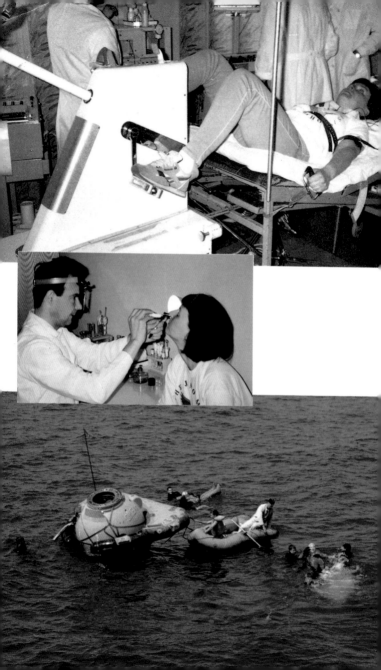

Opposite page
Above Helen undergoes the bicycle stress test, to check heart rate, blood pressure and breathing
Centre Yet another nasal examination
Below Sea training in the event of a splash landing

Right Tim and Helen just before a simulated training exercise

Below Helen in weightless training

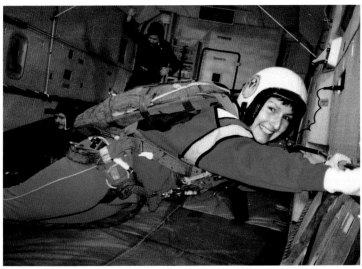

Above The Soyuz Rocket

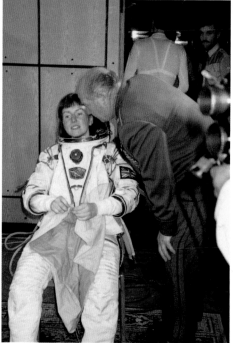

Left Suiting up on launch day: a final piece of advice from Alexei Leonov

Right Waving goodbye on the steps up to the gantry: (bottom to top) Sergei, Helen and Tolya

Below First view of Earth from space

Above Tolya and Sergei in the command module shortly after jettisoning the final rocket stage and becoming weightless

Below Our first dinner table on Soyuz: the packet containing the fork is stuck on with Velcro. A tube, tins and packets of food are held under elastic straps

Fortunately for art and politics, perhaps, you will also find others whose early years were altogether more interesting and who have better stories to tell about themselves. There is something that happened to me, though, that will not happen to most people: one day I climbed into a rocket and flew into space.

When I think back over the years before that happened, I have to face a dilemma which many people, particularly the journalists who have been assigned to write about me, have found partly intriguing and partly frustrating. My past and my present seem not to be connected logically. I am the first to admit that my childhood was uneventful (though never, to me, dull). Since then, things have been a little different.

Many times I have had variations of the same question put to me. What is it that happened to you, people ask, that made you into an astronaut?

The question seems to imply, though most people are too polite to spell it out, that a quarter-century of ordinariness is not a fit preparation for a job as unusual as being an astronaut. In this context, 'unusual' is probably taken to mean exciting, dangerous and glamorous.

One of the singular aspects of the astronaut job is that it forces you to look back on your own past in just this way. For instance, are solicitors, miners or hairdressers asked to locate and describe the single signifying deed or event that made them take up their careers?

Confronting this, as I have had to do ever since my return from space, I think the question is based on a misapprehension. This is to do with the job itself, rather than with those who do it. What I learnt was that although the job can certainly be dangerous, and sometimes exciting, it is not at all glamorous.

What it actually requires (in no particular order of importance) is good health, fitness, the ability to get on with other people and to work in a team. In the special case of the Anglo-Soviet mission in which I took part, it also required the ability to learn Russian quickly and to have a degree in a technical subject.

Good health is not something you can go out and get. Some
people are naturally healthy, others are not. I happen to be one of
the healthy ones. I had all the usual childhood diseases, but since
then have barely known illness. I don't suffer from headaches,
backache, indigestion, cramp, seasickness. I fall asleep instantly
and wake up without feeling groggy. Head-colds and flu touch
me, but only lightly.

Unlike good health, fitness is a condition which can be
attained by most people who want it. Before I went to Russia I
was probably more fit than most people, but not by a huge
degree. I have always enjoyed sport and physical exercise, but
having a job and other interests meant that I did not spend all my
energy on a sports field. The first serious physical training that I
undertook was in the Soviet Union, when I started the astronaut
training; until then I had never worked out or used weights.
After a few months in Russia, with plenty of exercise and regular
work in a gymnasium, I was pretty fit and probably stronger
than most people of my age and general size. You can be healthy
without being fit and (a bit more difficult) unhealthy but fit, but
to be an astronaut you have to be blessed with good health *and* be
in top physical condition.

An ability to get on with people is also something innate that
cannot easily be trained for. Again, I've always been lucky in
that I seem to hit it off with most people. Related to this is the
ability to work in a team. By this I don't mean the English jolly
hockey-sticks kind of thing, but a much simpler feeling that
everyone you're working with has the same wishes at heart, that
you're all heading in the same direction and that other people
depend on you as much as you depend on them. A space mission
would be dangerous if manned exclusively by 'top gun' fighter-
pilot jocks or rugged individualists of the lone-yachtsman type.
If astronauts don't work together, they put each other's lives in
jeopardy.

Part of the 'team spirit' I had to take on, and incredibly quickly
too, was to learn to speak Russian. This was not merely a

question of learning a few tourist phrases: the training and all our technical lectures were given in Russian. This problem obviously would not have arisen if I had been training in my own country, or with NASA, but I was in Russia and it was in the Soviet space program I was taking part. Before I went to Moscow I spoke no Russian and as soon as I got there I discovered that few, *very few*, of the people around me spoke English. This is not an exaggeration: even the man who taught us to speak Russian did not himself speak English! Once again, I was fortunate in that learning a language has never presented me with any particular problem.

Of all the conditions, only the required university degree in science was at all selective or restrictive. Fitness can be gained, the rest are innate . . . and even these could be overcome to some extent by someone determined enough; I am hardly the only person in Britain to have left university with a degree in a technical subject.

The point for me is not that my profoundly ordinary childhood qualified me in some unusual way to become an arstronaut, but that ordinary qualities are arguably amongst the best for the job. I did not know I was growing up to do the job I did. I did not even aspire to do that job. When the opportunity of the job came up, though, I was, quite unexpectedly, ready to do it.

3

2 DAYS

Soyuz

For two and a half hours after the successful completion of the launch we remained strapped to our seats in the Soyuz command capsule, working our way down the seemingly endless checklist while we floated serenely through our first two orbits of the Earth. We had to be certain no damage had been sustained during the launch. Was the on-board computer working as it should? Had the solar panels unfolded properly, and was the craft now rotating at the right speed to keep them directed towards the sun? Was the capsule pressurized correctly? Were the communications antennae all working?

Everything that could be checked was checked and, although after two and a half hours of this you feel you've checked every last rivet, there are actually many parts of the craft you have to take on trust. Two days later, when we were trying to make an automatic docking with Mir, one of the guidance antennae we couldn't check did fail.

Throughout all this we were still in our spacesuits, and strapped into our seats to stop us floating away. Before the launch I had assumed that getting out of the spacesuit would be a priority, but now we were weightless it was really not at all uncomfortable to wear. In addition, because we were not being pressed down into the seats by gravity or by the acceleration of the rocket and because we were able to loosen the straps a little, the suit ventilator could at last work more efficiently. The pool of perspiration that had gathered in the small of my back quickly evaporated and within a few minutes of being weightless I felt cool and comfortable all over. Also, the strain of having to reach for things, pushing all the time against the reinforcements inside the suit, felt much reduced.

One of the minor surprises of the Soyuz is that you would think that the constructors, after so many launches and with so much experience to hand, would have designed the inside of the command capsule ergonomically. This is far from true. The controls and instruments you have to reach for during the launch are at all angles and positions, there are sharp corners, and bits tacked on top of other bits. There was something gratifyingly *low*-tech about this utilitarian cockpit. Of course, once we were weightless it didn't matter so much, but under the pull of gravity some of the controls are hard to get at when you're in a spacesuit.

By about 6 p.m. (we stayed on Earth time, based on the time zone in Moscow) we had finished all the checks and were able to move up to the orbital capsule. I say 'up', because although vertical and horizontal directions have no meaning in space, we always thought of the orbital capsule as being above the command capsule, and spoke of the latter as being 'downstairs'. We were all eager by now to get out of the seats and be free of the spacesuits. After the cramped discomforts of the command capsule, the extra area above us seemed vast.

We wriggled out of the suits as quickly as possible and for several minutes we just floated happily around in our 'whites', the snug-fitting long johns and T-shirts. This was a period of the flight when mission control left us alone, and I was glad of it. In absolute terms the orbital capsule is not big. Had we been on Earth it would have felt like a tiny boxroom crammed with equipment, but once you are in space the weightlessness liberates you from the confines of a floor and gives you three dimensions in which to move around. The command capsule, though in fact somewhat larger, paradoxically never gave us this

DIAGRAM 2 – SOYUZ TM

1 Androgynous peripheral docking system
2 Orbital module
3 Descent vehicle
4 Instrument-assembly module
5 Solar panels
6 VHF radio station antennas on the frequency of 121,75 Mhz
7 Apollo VHF radio station antennas on the frequencies of 259,7 Mhz and 296,8 Mhz
8 Antennas of the radio and television system
9 Antennas of the command radio link and trajectory measurements
10 Antennas of the radio telemetry system
11 Antenna used to communicate with Earth
12 Docking target
13 On-board orientation lights
14 Flashing light beacons
15 Sun sensor
16 Ion orientation sensor
17 Infra-red orientation sensor
18 Optical orientator
19 Approach and orientation engines
20 Orientation engines
21 Approach-correcting engines
22 Hatch for the crew ingress
23 External TV camera
24 Windows

Main Characteristics

Crew	3 people
Spacecraft mass	7070 kg
Recoverable capsule mass	3000 kg
Length of the spacecraft	6.98 m
Maximum diameter	2.72 m
Solar batteries span	10.6 m
Rocket-carrier type	'SOYUZ'

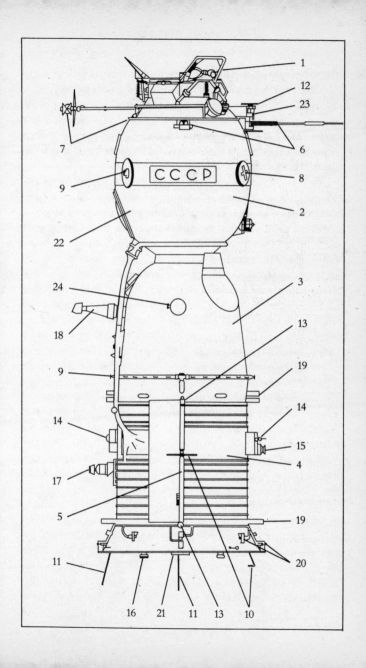

feeling of spaciousness: the presence of the seats and the controls around them imposed a sort of floor-based aspect to the area.

That first hour in the orbital capsule was pleasant for all of us; we remarked on the same feeling, that we were exploring a new home. Here was where they had stacked our belongings, the scientific experiments, here were our sleeping bags, our food, the drinking water . . . the toilet!

Also, for Tolya and myself, it was our first experience of real weightlessness. There had been the weightless training sessions in aircraft of course, but the longest period of time that our aircraft could simulate weightlessness was just over twenty seconds. Anyway, on those flights we were dressed in bulky flight clothes, including parachutes, were overseen by instructors and had specific tasks to carry out in a short time. Here in the capsule we were in a weightless state, floating contented and unhurried, lightly dressed, warm. We could move about at will, learn to spin and twist, try it out properly and find the measure of how hard we needed to push ourselves away to move safely across to the other side of the capsule.

As a general rule, now in the orbital capsule and later in the Mir space station, all astronauts did everything together, casually and naturally, on the whole preferring the company of each other to being alone. But there was one small matter that inevitably divided us, or at least in Soyuz divided me from the men.

Not long after we had shed our spacesuits, Tolya and Sergei said that they wanted to use the toilet. On the station the toilet has a door, so privacy is no different from what we expect on Earth, but there is no room for a separate toilet compartment in Soyuz. It is simply stored neatly behind a panel and pulled out when required. I returned to the command capsule for a few minutes and stared out of the window at the view below. When they had finished they offered to change places, but I didn't yet feel the need. I was seriously dehydrated anyway, after all that time inside the spacesuit.

Back in the orbital capsule Sergei gave us the first of several small lessons about the difference between spaceflight theory and spaceflight practice. We were all desperate for a drink of water, so we pressurized the water tank and looked around for our carefully labelled individual mouthpieces. Entire lectures had been devoted to the care and use of one's personal drinking mouthpiece, with much emphasis on hygiene and the risk of spreading germs.

Sergei just grinned. 'No need for all that,' he said. 'Open your mouth.'

He pressed open the valve and a shimmering, wobbling sphere of pure water flew gracefully across towards me. I closed my mouth around it and was rewarded with a delicious explosion of cold water!

After this, we always drank water in the same way and never used the special mouthpieces at all. The point is that on Earth they think about the dangers, the risks, the awful disasters that can happen if anything goes wrong and so they try to drum in a sense of super-safety in their astronauts. To ground-based instructors the idea of globules of water flying freely about the inside of a spacecraft is immensely dangerous. They imagine valuable equipment being wrecked, short circuits in the computers, power failures and so on. When you're up there in space, though, you can see what you're doing, know what the risks are. You're highly trained and (more important) highly motivated. No astronaut is going to fire a jet of drinking water into the cabin, then lose interest and go to do something else, while the globules head relentlessly towards the nearest piece of electronic equipment!

Although it didn't signify a huge gulf between ground control and astronauts, we came across several more similar examples of this during the rest of the flight.

One such concerned the obsession of Earthbound psychologists with the drastic effects weightlessness was thought to have on our sense of equilibrium. Mission control was continuing to leave us to our own devices, so I drifted up to the blister window, something that had been newly introduced to the Soyuz craft. Its actual purpose is to enable one of the crew to get a clearer eyeline on the space station during docking, in case of equipment failure, but what I soon discovered was that if I pressed my face against the glass I could see back along the side of the Soyuz craft itself. There's something about being able to *see* your own craft! I found it ravishing to look at, bathed as it was in the brilliant, unfiltered sunlight and set off starkly against the black of outer space.

The blister window also gave an unparalleled view of the Earth's surface and it was here that my passion for staring down at the world really began. So much of my time in space was to be spent looking down in fascination from one of the windows. I never tired of the view and astronauts who have been in space far longer than I was say that the attraction never fades.*

In these first couple of hours in the Soyuz I was mainly learning how it felt to be in space, weightless in a capsule, and the differences there were in the way our outer reality is perceived. I have already mentioned, for instance, that the craft was rotating slowly so that the solar panels, now unfolded, would receive the maximum amount of energy from the sun to convert into electricity. When I first went to the blister window I stared down at the ground and in order to keep orientated in the same way I instinctively inched my way round the rim. I looked back inside the capsule and everything suddenly seemed upside-down!

This kind of thing is a little distracting and quite fascinating to experiment with, but it isn't at all traumatic. Here is the difference between the theories of the psychologists on Earth and astronauts' actual experiences. We were warned about getting confused and given simple techniques to reassure us of our equilibrium, but it was all a lot of fuss about nothing. I simply spun around and moved away, thinking sardonically

* See Chapter Seven.

how disappointing we would be to any psychologist who ever found out how easy and intuitive we all found weightlessness to be.

A little later, playing around with the weightless condition, I curled myself into a little ball in the centre of the capsule and tried to stay as stationary as possible. It was relatively easy to get into a position from which I didn't drift to one side, but there was nothing I could do about the fact that the craft was rotating around me.

Of course, there *were* orientations that we adopted in space. I have already mentioned that we worked on the basis that the orbital capsule was 'above' the command capsule. There was a practical reason for this. It was, after all, a part of a powerful rocket and from time to time, when we had to use the main engine, the craft emphatically felt as if it had a top and a bottom. For most of the time, though, we simply drifted around contentedly, completely at ease with the situation. Later, I found this even more true within the Mir space station, where concepts of horizontal and vertical, up and down were virtually irrelevant to the way we lived and worked or moved around.

We took our spacesuits back down to the command capsule, where they could be spread out to be dried (we would need them again, but after the launch they were soaked with sweat), then went back up for dinner. By this time all three of us were ravenous! Mission control was still leaving us alone, so we cracked open several tins of meat and fish and toothpaste-type tubes of runnier stuff like cream cheese and vegetable purées. It was one of the most delicious meals of my life. We ate the lot, feeling gluttonous and heady. For refreshment we drank fruit juice (also from tubes) and went back to playing around with the water.

There wasn't complete radio silence during this long and unusual evening. We spoke to mission control whenever we were over Russia, but most of the traffic between us was simply confirming that everything was OK, that we were settling down all right and so on. Towards the end of the evening, though, we had to increase our orbit, as we were still at an altitude significantly lower than Mir's orbit.

Officially, all three of us should have gone down to the command capsule to be in our seats during the engine impulse, but only two people are actually needed for the checks. We discussed this briefly and came to the conclusion that the hassle of getting all three of us into our seats outweighed the strict observance of the rules. Sergei and Tolya went down to the command capsule, while I stayed upstairs, keeping in touch with what was going on by wearing headphones with a long extension lead down to my seat.

Before the first impulse, Sergei said, 'Watch out when the engine comes on!'

I knew of course to take literally, and seriously, any warning Sergei gave me, but already I had started to fall prey to the seductive ease of the weightless life. Waiting for the engine to fire, I took a casual grip on the nearest bit of the spacecraft to me. Seconds later I was hanging on for dear life, my feet swinging embarrassingly through the hatch to the command capsule, as the large and powerful rocket below me (distinctly *below* me now!) lifted us another 30 kilometres or so further into space.

A short while later, when Sergei fired the engine for a second orbital increase, I was braced more securely against the thrust . . .

With these orbital adjustments successfully completed, we were all exhausted. It was 10.30 p.m., Moscow time, and we were ready for bed. Tolya and I unpacked the sleeping bags while Sergei, still in the command capsule, was in contact with mission control.

Tolya said as we were getting the sleeping bags ready, 'Have you noticed how much cooler it is down there?' I said I had. Sergei came back just then. According to the rules, one of us was supposed to sleep in the command capsule, leaving the other two up above. The psychologists had tried to persuade us of this by saying, 'It'll be less cramped if you spread out, and give you a break from being with the others all the time.' But when we came to it we looked at each other and it was obvious no one wanted to volunteer to go downstairs alone. We liked being together! We wanted to stay together! Sergei, who had been through this before, showed us the best way to get the three sleeping bags into position and no more mention was made of these rules.

When the bags were all tied in place (mine was opposite the window, Sergei's was beside mine, and Tolya's faced us both; we arranged it so that our heads were 'up' in relation to the capsule), Sergei returned briefly to the command capsule and told mission control we were tired and wanted to get some sleep. I don't remember him returning; I fell asleep instantly.

(Under normal conditions on Earth our bodies are subject to gravity, and blood is pulled towards the feet. Our hearts pump against that, circulating blood around our bodies and keeping it in our heads. Now, because I was weightless, my heart was still pumping away against a force that no longer existed. Body fluids tended to move towards my head, making my face appear fat and puffy. It was uncomfortable for a few days. My eyes felt as though they were bulging because the fluid inside them was under a higher pressure than they were used to. There is a general 'full of a cold' feeling, until the body, wonderfully adaptive as it is, excretes this 'extra' fluid and a feeling of normality returns. This means that astronauts tend to lose 'weight' during the first few days in space, and the diet must take this into account. It isn't just water that is lost from the body, but vital minerals. However, to ease the discomfort of blocked noses and bulging eyes, we wore elastic straps, braslets, around the tops of our legs. By overcoming venous pressure somewhat, they restricted the flow of body fluids from the legs, but were not tight enough to stop fluids from going into the legs.)

On Earth we rely on wind and convection to move air around. In space there is no wind as such, and if you're weightless there is no convection – hot air does not rise. This means that the carbon dioxide that we exhaled could easily mount up around the breather's face, unless the air is circulated properly. Cocooned inside my sleeping bag there would be no means of fanning fresh air into it from the capsule. Not wanting the problem of disposing of the first dead human body in space, Tolya decided to reach inside my bag and pull me out by the chin!

When I came to, I had a fleeting impression that I had somehow turned upside-down in the night; that is, that my head was towards the command capsule below us. As Tolya gently pulled my head into the open air, though, I immediately reoriented. Pressure of blood in your head normally only builds up, on Earth, when you stand on your head. Because I had loosened the braslets in the night, and the pressure had built up, my drowsy state tricked me into thinking I must have been on my head! This problem gradually went away over the next few days, as my body acclimatized to being in space.

After breakfast I hovered by the window and cleaned my teeth. A Soviet space 'toothbrush' is a piece of muslin impregnated with minty toothpaste, which you slip over your finger. Delicious! Below me was the Pacific Ocean, slipping by, slowly, slowly.

We had to clean up the capsule a little, because we hadn't been too careful with crumbs. On Mir the problem of bits of food floating around doesn't really arise, because the station is so well ventilated and the air filtered, but in the Soyuz there were no decent filters on the fans. In our enjoyment of the food we had broken the bread with a little too much abandon, and now the three of us collected the bits that we came across, hanging forlornly in the capsule.

In the command capsule the spacesuits were still drying. Tolya and Sergei went down there to make another correctional engine impulse, this one only 3 seconds in duration. As before, I stayed upstairs in the orbital capsule, braced against the thrust.

After this we checked our oxygen level. This was because of

something we had discovered towards the end of the previous day. It turned out that during the launch the oxygen inside our command module had been increasing in pressure by about 1 mm of mercury per minute, which is a terrific increase. During the launch we checked for a *decrease* in pressure and had this occurred we should have known about it immediately. We lacked alarms for pressure increases, though. Had the oxygen level kept on increasing at that rate it would have become dangerous inside the spacecraft, because too high an oxygen level leads to the risk of fire and explosion. Mission control's theory, when the fault was discovered, was that one of the oxygen valves must have been fouled with dust, but that as soon as we were in space the dust had been sucked away by the vacuum and the valve closed, stopping the flow of oxygen. If this hadn't cleared itself in time the only remedy would have been to open a hole in the hull of the spacecraft to release the oxygen-rich air. Not only was this dangerous in itself but it meant we would have had to live inside our spacesuits and make an emergency re-entry. This was a serious problem and we nearly didn't make it past the first orbit! Afterwards, we kept a wary eye on such measurements.

We spent the whole of this second day heading slowly towards our rendezvous with Mir, giving us plenty of opportunity to get used to the little practices you have to develop in weightlessness. Anything left unattached drifts away and so you get into the habit of holding it down in some fashion. Many of the working surfaces have elasticated tags across them, allowing you to slip loose objects underneath. In addition, the walls of the craft are lined with soft velcro, and most of the movable items on board have a strip of hard, hooked velcro, so a quick press against the nearest wall will generally find a place to leave something.

I also used this second day to get accustomed to using the on-board toilet.

One of the curiosities of being an astronaut is that a lot of people you meet (who under other social circumstances would presumably not even think of raising the subject) are fascinated by one's bowel and bladder movements and how you cope with them in space. The answer (for some of these same people, I imagine) is rather disappointingly ordinary.

On Russian spacecraft they install a fairly conventional privy. This differs from toilets on the ground in only two significant ways. First, there obviously has to be some way of keeping yourself in the right position and orientation, so that you don't drift away before you're finished. Secondly, instead of using water to flush away the bodily wastes it uses air: you switch it on, hold yourself in place and a steady suction of air does the rest. Everything is collected in a container 'underneath'. (On Mir, intended for long-term use, the liquid wastes are recycled. Urine is filtered and purified enough to be used as drinking water. If, as was the case while I was in space, drinking water is abundant, water separated from urine is electrolyzed. The molecule H_2O is split into its elemental components of hydrogen and oxygen. Hydrogen, not required, is eventually vented into space, but the oxygen is used to breathe.)

The only thing that is really different is that you realize how dependent on gravity you become and that when you're in space it seems to take slightly more effort to force everything out. Even this is something you adapt to: after the first day it all felt completely normal to me.

Something else I had to force was my appetite. After that first meal on the day of the launch I was never hungry in space. Time for meals came around and we would open the sealed packages, more from a sense of duty than anything else. Once we started eating, though, hunger arrived! We would wolf down everything we could find, then stop just as suddenly. I always knew when I'd had enough: I was full and could eat no more. Even the hassle of finding a waste-bin for the final, leftover portion of bread was worth it – I did not want one gram of food more. Tolya and Sergei said they felt exactly the same way about food.

We woke late on our second morning in space (although this time I wasn't at risk from suffocation and I suffered no delusions about being upside-down). It was dark when we awoke: 9.30 a.m., and it was the middle of the night! A little bit surprising, until you remember that darkness for us lasted about forty minutes and happened sixteen times a day. As we floated out of our sleeping bags and started to put them away, dawn broke.

Somewhat guiltily we went straight down to the command capsule to contact mission control and then went back upstairs for breakfast. According to our printed schedule we were supposed to do these the other way around, but we didn't like to admit we had wanted to sleep on.

It was now Monday, and later in the day we were due to dock with the space station. I decided to wash my hair and did so. This is easy in a spacecraft: they supply damp cloths specifically for that purpose. By the time I had finished it was night again and I discovered that the windows made excellent mirrors.

All day I felt excited by the prospect of reaching the space station, but in general we had a lot of preparations and checklists to get through. As late as possible, we struggled into our spacesuits again and crammed into the command capsule seats.

It was on our approach to Mir, about 200 kilometres away, that we discovered one of the antennae on the Soyuz craft had failed. This gave wide-range readings on the approach to the space station, and was used in the automatic guidance system. There was no immediate danger in this, because we had been trained to take over control of the Soyuz and dock manually, but it reminded us of an aspect of our mission which had been contentious from well before the launch.

The point was that an earlier unmanned mission had experienced some difficulty docking with Mir. This was because of the failure of an antenna on the space station itself (although ironically this particular piece of equipment worked perfectly for us). While our mission was in the planning stage it therefore seemed more likely that a manual docking would have to be attempted. In our crew Sergei was the experienced cosmonaut, while for Tolya, who was the commander, the pilot, it was the first flight. The commander of the back-up crew, Tim Mace's crew, had been in space before and would therefore in theory be better placed to take on a manual docking.

It was just one of those many uncertainties in the weeks leading up to the flight that made it all extremely nerve-racking. As events turned out, of course, it was my crew that was chosen for the flight, and Tolya, given the task, proved himself to be more than capable.

There is in existence some newsreel film of our docking which shows the reaction of the people in mission control, clapping, cheering and hugging each other as the two craft make contact. Because of this film, I am often asked if the docking was traumatic to go through and if we realized how close to disaster we were.

Disappointingly, for those who like dramatic or death-defying endeavours, this is one of many similar cases where things from the outside appear different from the way they seem to those on the spot.

True, if we had not docked successfully we would have had to try again with all the delays it would have caused and the doubts it might have raised, and if we had failed on the second attempt we would have had to abort the whole mission and return to Earth. If you miss by a mile you have another go. If you miss by six inches you have two badly damaged spacecraft and five dead cosmonauts. None of this was good to think about.

On the other hand, the three of us had worked together for months, we were highly trained, and furthermore we had been trained to deal with just this eventuality.

The docking procedure is slow, much slower than it looks on film. For one thing the station is in contact with our instruments for a long time before we physically make contact;

I even caught a glimpse of it through my window, a brilliant-white T-shape, apparently so tiny and distant, making me catch my breath.

Once we were in the immediate vicinity it was really a matter of making the two craft line up correctly on each other, then guide one into the other. For this the Soyuz has a male docking cone and the station a female shape to accept it. When contact was made our cone had sensors which determined exactly where the docking was made, and the craft was then able to turn automatically to match. There is actually a fair amount of margin of error, allowing for angle of approach, angle of inclination and so on.

We were aiming for the docking-port at the point where the stem of the T meets the crossbar. This is one of the preferred ports for docking with Mir (the port on the Kvant module is also often used), because although there are others (one at each end of the T crossbar) these have the additional risk that the station could start spinning. It could be corrected, of course, but it would use up valuable time and fuel.

My rôle during docking was to act as Tolya's assistant, rather like a theatre sister helps a surgeon. I was also operating the TV cameras because my control panel had the means of selecting the wide-angle or narrow-angle lens, depending on how close we were, or what Tolya actually wanted to see. Mission control stayed quiet through the operation, leaving us to get on with it, but they would have been listening closely to everything that happened.

When the docking was complete, we heard in our headsets the noise of clapping and cheering in mission control, oddly underlining the fact that what we had just done was fraught with dangers. However, I can only tell my own version of events: for me it would be misleading to make a drama where none existed, because the docking was carried out according to the book. The three of us worked as a team, each of us doing our own individual jobs, relying on the other two to do theirs. We knew what a mistake by any of us could mean, but nothing went wrong, and we were doing what we had been sent into space to do.

However, anyone who has been part of a team that has worked hard towards a single goal, and has overcome problems in a united effort, will understand the overwhelming spirit of closeness and joy that engulfed us when we felt the bump as Soyuz and Mir made contact.

4

13,000 TO 4

Selection Process

One pleasant evening at the end of June 1989 I was driving home from the Mars factory in Slough, listening to the car radio. While I sat in a traffic jam I flicked through the radio stations trying to find something to listen to. Suddenly, my attention was grabbed by a male voice. It said: 'Astronaut wanted. No experience necessary.'

I can no longer remember why I was driving home that day, instead of making my regular trip to Birkbeck College. It actually made a difference, because when I was driving into London I usually kept the radio tuned to one channel for traffic news. On this particular evening, going to my flat in Surbiton, I was trying to find some music. One of the channels I happened to tune into carried this advertisement, and once I heard that singular headline I had to listen to the rest.

I know, with hindsight, that the minute or so I spent listening to this advertisement is the crucial, pivotal moment in my life. After it, nothing from my old life could ever quite be the same again; everything that has happened since has been coloured, directly or indirectly, by it. It was the rarest of moments and by twisting the radio's volume control so I could hear a little more clearly, I was seizing it. However, at the time it did not feel quite so grand. It simply felt as if I were driving home from work on a warm summer's evening, moving in rush-hour traffic along the A308 Staines bypass and listening to a rather cleverly written job advertisement on the radio.

I had no background in space research. I had never harboured ambitions to go into space. It had never occurred to me that I could or would ever wish to go into space, let alone be able to. What struck me, though, were the remarkably straightforward requirements for the basic qualifications: the job was open to Britons aged between twenty-one and forty; applicants required a formal scientific training, a proven ability to learn a foreign language, and should have a high standard of medical fitness. That was all.

I thought: that's me! I'm all those things!

It was a distracting and intriguing thought: that by these fairly broad criteria I was already, without realizing it, in a particular segment of the population any of whose members could become an astronaut.

They gave out a phone number at the end of the advertisement and when I had to stop a few moments later at a set of traffic lights I scribbled it down on the back of an old petrol receipt.

This was not a particularly restless stage in my life. I was happy in my job, but I was certainly not in a position to think of that job as forming a career for the rest of my life. I was not actively seeking another job, but had I seen one advertised in a newspaper I might well have written off to find out more about it. In my private life I had a boyfriend, but neither of us had given much thought to settling down together. I had bought somewhere to live, but it was just an ordinary studio flat in a London suburb, which I liked well enough but to which I had no great long-term attachment. In brief, although I was not actively seeking change in my life, I was definitely receptive to it.

Even so, this advertisement did not have an immediately transforming effect on me. Life went on in its familiar way and although I had the phone number I didn't bother to call it straight away. The seized moment began to slacken in my grasp. I finally got around to doing something about it when the weekend came.

The voice at the other end took down my name, address, age and brief details of my degree. Then they asked a few questions. They wanted to know about the languages I spoke (French and German) and whether I had working knowledge of them or if they were just left over from school. Also, was I still doing an actual practical scientific job with my hands, rather than a desk job?

Two or three days later I received an application form. I glanced through it with some interest, realized that to do it justice I would need to take three or four hours over it and slipped it into my briefcase until I could find the time.

That time did not make itself available straight away. I kept putting it off, rather resenting all the work I would have to do for what seemed, frankly, a highly remote chance. The form stayed in my briefcase for ages, probably two or three weeks.

One evening I was at Birkbeck and I needed to check the experimental work I'd been doing the night before. I was researching the luminescence of rare-earth ions in crystals and in glasses. I was fascinated to see light being emitted by substances when they were bombarded by electrons, but I was particularly interested in how some of these ions could store energy from the electrons and transfer that energy to other ions, which would then emit their own luminescence.

I pulled out my papers from the briefcase and this form slipped out too. I saw it and thought, 'I'm *never* going to get that done!' I left it there on the bench while I switched on my photo-multiplier cooler, to cool down my apparatus before starting. I came back, and started to go through what I'd done the night before so that I knew exactly where I was up to and which crystal I wanted to look at that night.

I saw the form again. The closing date was in two or three days' time. I realized that if I didn't take the time to do it then, I never would. I picked it up, put it down again. I thought, 'Why waste a whole evening when I could be doing my research?'

I glanced through it, intending at last to throw it away, but then I went and turned off my photo-multiplier cooler and sat down at my desk. Instead of doing my research work that night I filled out the form, and posted it on the way home.

I would usually make a photocopy of any application form I sent in, but, as some indicator of how low I rated my chances with this astronaut job, I was so sure that I wouldn't even get to the first interview stage that I didn't bother. Having said that, though, I did fill out the form properly and gave it my undivided attention for the three hours it took.

I carried on with my ordinary life and, because I simply did not expect to hear from them again, I forgot all about it.

Unknown to me at the time, an arithmetical process had begun, a series of numerical eliminations. I later found out that my phonecall that Saturday morning was one of more than thirteen thousand similar calls over the two- or three-week period when the lines were open. The simple questions on the telephone filtered out more than half of those and doubtless a huge number of people never got around to completing the form, because applications were received from only five and a half thousand people. From these, a hundred and fifty were selected.

The information that I was one of them came in a phonecall one weekday morning. I was asleep; Mars Confectionery operates twenty-four hours a day and, because I was single and could be flexible with my time, I had volunteered to work some nights to oversee a number of changes on a production line. That morning I wasn't expecting anyone to ring and I let it go on for a while. I finally picked it up.

A woman's voice said, 'I'm telephoning on behalf of Air Vice-Marshal Peter Howard, and would like to ask if you would come for a medical for the Anglo-Soviet Juno Space Mission.' She asked if I could be available on a particular date.

I looked in my diary and said, 'Yes, that's fine.' I scribbled the date into the diary, then put down the phone and went back to bed. I fell asleep instantly.

I got up again that night. While I was dressing to go to work, a thought snapped through my mind: 'That's funny, I had a really weird dream today!' I went back to my diary and found I'd actually written it in. I went to work and halfway through the night, during our break, I said to the guy I was working with, 'I got a phonecall today; they've asked me to go for some medicals for this space mission.' And he laughed! I laughed too.

I went along to the BUPA building in London's Pentonville Road in the first week in August. Already an air of unreality had entered the proceedings because here I was, in effect, applying for a different job and I'd already told my current boss at Mars what I was doing. (He too had laughed, but told me to make the most of it all. No one was taking it seriously, least of all me.)

They were carrying out the first medicals over a three-week period, splitting us up into small groups and testing two groups each day. Each of the groups was tested in tandem, one going through the medicals while the other took the psychological tests, then vice versa in the afternoon. All the medicals were fairly standard: eyesight, peripheral vision, hearing, chest, nerves, then on to a treadmill for tests on heart-rate recovery and oxygen uptake. (I imagine these are exactly the kinds of tests BUPA routinely carry out on management personnel who are being enrolled into company medical schemes.) The psychologicals were also standard multi-choice, odd-one-out and perception tests. There was a manual dexterity test, too: we had to go to a board studded with pegs, then pick up tiny washers and drop them over the pegs. Another test involved pushing pins into little holes in the board. By common consent amongst the people I was being tested with, it all made up for a pretty mundane kind of afternoon.

One feature distinguished this from what I imagine is an ordinary day at BUPA: some journalists from the British-published magazine *Soviet Weekly* turned up and asked us a few rather general questions. I'd never spoken to journalists before and found the experience rather strange. I couldn't see the point of it, but with hindsight I do now wonder if the Juno organizers were giving us a first test dip into the shallows of what later turned out to be a fairly rough media sea.

At the end of it all I went home, thinking, 'Hmm . . . I didn't do that very well.' I'd had a day off work and met a few people I hadn't known before, but I assumed that that was the last I would hear of the matter.

Something was changing inside me, though. I still considered that I was highly unlikely to be selected, but now the difference was that I *wanted* to go into space. I had not realized before that such a prospect was within reach, at least in theory. In the past it had seemed to me that the people who went into space were, well, astronauts, and because I was not an astronaut then I never gave it a thought.

I was discovering now that astronauts were made and not born, and that in previous lives they were sometimes teachers, doctors, soldiers, university lecturers, scientists, just like some of the people I had briefly met at BUPA. Just like me.

Six weeks earlier I would never have even thought about space; now I could think of little else. I wanted to be chosen and to go into space, but wishing alone could not make it happen. It seemed that everything was already determined, a set of criteria had been laid down, and it was all a matter of chance whether it would be this woman or that man who lived up to them.

Behind the scenes, or at least behind *my* scenes, because I knew none of this until a long time later, the numerical process was continuing. The one hundred and fifty medical reports were being closely examined and from them was emerging a long shortlist of thirty-two candidates.

The phone rang unexpectedly one afternoon at work, a couple

of weeks after the BUPA medicals. Would I come for the next stage of selection, a meeting at Brunel University? I hesitated for all of a millisecond, then said yes.

There had been a great deal of media attention from the start and by reading newspaper reports I had begun to work out for myself something about how the mission was being structured and financed.

The Juno mission was planned from the outset to be a commercial enterprise. The money required by Glavkosmos, the Soviet Space Administration, to take a British astronaut to the Mir station in 1991 was $12 million, or about £7.5 million at the rate then current. Further costs would increase this. Experiments would have to be developed, then these and other requirements would have to be integrated with the Soviets' own work on the space station. The total cost was expected to be around £16 million.

All this money would be raised in Britain by industrial sponsorship. The process of choosing the astronaut would be highly publicized, as would the personality of the final candidate himself. A company, Antequera Ltd, was set up to administer the selection of the astronaut and the mission itself, and the final aspects would be underwritten by the Moscow Narodny Bank. Although this bank is Russian-owned, it is run as a commercial enterprise in the City of London, and staffed by banking professionals. The bank did not intend to manage the mission; that would be the responsibility of the people working for Antequera.

As the selection process went on, this background had an increasing effect on the applicants. The commercial nature was out in the open from the start, and as we first met and had dealings with the people who were running Antequera we began to understand what was expected of us.

I was only just sensing some of this when I went along to Brunel University during the last weekend in August, but it was then that our education began in earnest.

For us, the last thirty-two candidates, the first and most important step was meeting each other and starting to do a little quiet sizing up. First impressions convinced me yet again I was the odd one out! Everyone else seemed to be so highly qualified, already three-quarters of the way to being an astronaut. Of those who were scientists many seemed to be specializing in fields directly relevant to space travel and exploration. If they weren't scientists they were working in the aeronautical industry, or they lectured in space technology, or they were pilots. I met Tim Mace at Brunel; Tim was in the army, a pilot, an aeronautical engineer, and was Britain's skydiving champion. He had just managed to get back in time to Brunel from Spain, where he had been taking part in the world skydiving championships. After a short chat with him he seemed to me the obvious, stand-out candidate. He looked the part, spoke well, had blond hair, blue eyes. He was a little bit older than me, but very fit. Most of the others looked big and hunky, really fit and on the ball. What was I doing there? I was a research technologist at a confectionery company! I began to think some mistake had been made, that I was there because my papers had been mixed up with someone else's.

With the social ice cracked, if not exactly broken, we moved on to the more formal part of the evening. Several presentations from mission managers filled us in on a few practical details, and a solicitor retained by the mission sketched out for us the legal ramifications of what we were letting ourselves in for. We were warned, for instance, that if we had skeletons in the cupboard they were likely to come out. I can't speak for any of the others, but I felt fairly sanguine about all this. Nothing could detract from my wish to go into space! Already we were being treated a little like contestants in a TV game show, where the main prize is so dazzlingly attractive there is virtually no challenge, forfeit or even humiliation too great to deter the people who want to win it.

Professor Heinz Wolff, who was coordinating the scientific

element of the mission from Brunel, spoke next. He gave us some idea of what the technical experiments were likely to be about, but it was still a bit hazy at this stage. No firm sponsorship money had yet been offered, for instance. From other clues, we gained insights into some of the haste with which the arrangements had been made. They had, we learned, only signed the agreement with the Russians in June and the advertisement for the astronauts had been released the day after.

We all stayed overnight at Brunel and in the morning were taken by bus to the Royal Aeronautical Society in London. Someone pointed out that out of the thirty-two remaining candidates one-third were women, a proportion in which some newspapers were later to try to find some significance. (About one-third of the original hundred and fifty were also women.) The only salient point any of us could see in this was that all applicants had to have a scientific or technical degree and that the number of women coming out of universities with that kind of degree is considerably lower than one-third the number of men. In other words, as far as the Juno mission was concerned, the women appeared to have done rather better so far than the men.

Another presentation awaited us at the RAeS, this time by Air Vice-Marshal Peter Howard who spoke to us about the round of medical tests that was to follow. These were going to be thorough, to say the least, and Peter Howard obviously felt it was only fair to warn us. If the intention was to make the faint-hearted among us have second thoughts, it mostly failed. Only one person thought better of it and dropped out at this point.

If anything was likely to be more off-putting it was what happened next, although I don't suppose anyone organizing the mission would have seen it that way. With the presentation completed, we were ushered into another room where a huge press conference was waiting to begin. The world's press (or at least, what felt like a considerable chunk of it) descended on us. Unpractised and unprepared as we were, we had nothing to guide us but our own instincts.

Mine were fairly simple, and they followed a line of reasoning I was to use several more times in the weeks ahead: (1) Antequera has set this up; (2) I want to be selected and don't want to seem uncooperative; therefore (3) I'll swallow my pride and answer questions as openly as I can.

This was what I did and as far as I know it is what most of us did. These days, by dint of sheer experience, I've learnt that when you speak to a journalist you say what *you* want to say and try not to be sidetracked into the trivial stuff that inevitably comes up. This press conference, though, was the first experience for most of us, and we trotted into it like lambs to the slaughter.

Of course, the ten young women were instantly leapt upon, separated from the male applicants and lined up for a photo call. Everyone should have known that would happen. I let slip the information (to me, innocuous) that I worked for Mars, and instantly became 'the girl from Mars'. It seemed quite witty, the first two hundred times it was repeated. I wasn't the only one who spoke innocently to reporters and in the days and weeks that followed we were subjected in the media to every imaginable dull-witted play on words. Our hopes were soaring, while we reached for the stars and were boldly going. We were starry eyed or over the moon, taking small steps, flying high (or sometimes high-flying), and the whole lot of us had space fever. The point of this is not that we were lacking in sense of humour, but that it would have been welcome if someone had taken the trouble to think beyond the usual clichés.

Afterwards, I drifted home and went back to my job at Mars, but already things were changing. The national press highlighted the applicants as a group, but the local and regional press concentrated on the individuals who happened to have local and regional connections. I began to receive phonecalls at work from journalists, who expected an interview there and then, without preparation, while I was in the lab and with my colleagues around me. On one occasion I had a call which said, 'Oh, could you do an interview for the radio? You're on live, and we'll be talking to you straight after the next record.'

Obviously, my bosses noticed all the activity and I wasn't at all sure how they were taking it. Soon after the RAeS event, though, one of the managers approached me and asked me if I would mind if he sent a memo about what I was involved with to all the other Mars section managers. I tried to downplay it, but he was very supportive. Soon afterwards, the flier went around and from that point on I felt I had the whole company behind me. Much of what happened in the next few weeks was made possible by the liberal attitude of the Mars management to all the time I had to take off work, the journalists pestering the public relations department and so on.

I imagine that all over the country other applicants were experiencing much the same. What had started out as a bit of a punt, an intriguing distraction, a wacky job application, had now become not only highly serious but was also being carried out in the full glare of publicity. The stakes were much higher than any of us had realized. The publicity would fuel the sponsorship, but for most of the applicants it would inevitably mean rejection in public.

The winnowing down was continuing. The next set of medical tests was going to be gruelling and would involve a large number of X-rays, so a decision was made to treat the men and women differently. The men began their medical tests straight away, but the women were given the psychological tests first, the reasoning being that the doctors didn't want to subject the women to unnecessary X-rays.

These psychological tests were much more extensive than the earlier ones. They measured intelligence, mechanical and spatial reasoning, visual checking, dexterity and personality. Afterwards came an interview with an occupational psychologist, and this was followed by the presentation of a short talk, as a test of media skills. Finally, we were tested on what they called a 'Personal Values Inventory', which consisted of four dozen cards listing reasons for wanting to be an astronaut, to be sorted into order of priority. They included motives like the possible thawing of East–West relations, personal fame, money and the good of science. I tried to give answers that were true to myself (without trying to anticipate what I felt they might be expecting), and at the end came down with a slight emphasis on doing experiments and being a scientist. A close second was more simple, because by then I just wanted to be an astronaut. I wanted to blast off in a rocket, be up there in space, float around, see the Earth! I fancied going! Quite a long way down my list was that I wanted to be famous, to be the first Briton in space, and I placed financial reasons last.

Because of what happened to me later I was eventually given a copy of my results from these tests and I can see, from this distance, that I did not do awfully well. They seemed to like me all right and I did well with intelligence and mechanical reasoning, but I scored low on spatial reasoning (the ability to conceptualize objects rotating in 3-D), my presentation to the psychologist was a bit of an embarrassment and in general it was decided my psychological make-up was full of contradictions (loud, brash and assertive on one hand, committed, shy and friendly on the other).

Even so, I was deemed to have passed, and so I went forward to the next stage of tests.

The psychological checking had a radical effect on the number of candidates, in particular the women. Of the thirty-one who had reached the previous stage only twenty-two continued forward. Of these, three were women.

Now began the main battery of medical tests. The doctors had to be sure that we could cope with the training and the launch, that our bodies would be able to adapt well to weightlessness and then re-adapt to 1 g on Earth again. Also it was important that we would not become ill during training or in space, which might jeopardize the mission.

Without mincing words the tests were horrendous to endure.

For one thing, as a normally well person I had hardly had any contact with doctors since early childhood, and numerous diagnostic procedures often make the recipient feel worse than he had before entering hospital. The exquisite discomforts of barium meals, barium enemas and endoscopic probes of the intestine cannot be understated.

People who need such tests to find out what's wrong with them normally only have to endure one or two, and then spaced apart. Not only did we suffer many different kinds, they all came one after the other. It's painful, for example, to have your intestine probed with an endoscope, so you are normally given a shot of intravenous Valium beforehand. We had already been given Valium for the gastroscopy on our stomachs, though, and had to have the second probe without. In the same way, I had X-rays taken just after having had a heart monitor set up, so I had electrodes all over my chest which couldn't be taken off. My X-rays had little black dots all over them! All this was going on under a general edict not to eat; as well as being uncomfortable for most of the time we were also starving.

This kind of experience quickly creates a sense of team-spirit with the other victims. All ideas that we were basically in competition with each other were set aside early on. We were equals in this and we were all a little bit worried about what was going to happen next. The person in front would come out and say, 'Well, it's a bit sore, but, um, don't worry you'll be fine.' So you would go in, temporarily reassured, and as soon as it started you would think, 'Bloody hell, this hurts!' Later, you'd come out and say to the next guy, 'It's a bit sore, but don't worry. You'll be fine!'

In the middle of the first week, one of the other candidates and I were told we could go, so we crept away from the hospital, feeling a bit sore around the nether regions. We hadn't eaten or drunk anything except sips of water for more than thirty hours. We were really starving and we found a café. We sat down and perused the menu, but quickly came to the conclusion that we weren't really feeling all that well, so we had a cup of tea then went grimly home.

One evening, in spite of everything, I made an appointment with my dentist. One of the examinations had revealed a couple of fillings were needed, but more importantly that as three of my wisdom teeth still had not grown they might be a factor in whether or not I was chosen. My own dentist confirmed the position and she made me an appointment at the local hospital.

Back at the testing clinic the probing and sampling continued. One of the doctors said, presumably intending to amuse us, 'If there's an orifice anywhere in your body, you can be sure we will put something in, or take something out.' He did, and so did all the others; we remained largely unamused.

Because we were fit patients and therefore, so to speak, volunteers, it did sometimes seem as if the bond of confidentiality between doctor and patient had no meaning any more. One morning, while I was being prepared for an endoscope to be inserted into my rectum and large intestine, an area of my body I usually keep fairly private, a salesman from the company who made the fibre-optic probe walked in. He wanted to see how it performed. They asked me, 'Do you mind if this person watches?' My immediate reaction was to say, 'Yes, I bloody well do mind'; but I also felt I couldn't say that and it was going to be like this a lot in the future. Anyway how could I know who he really was? Maybe he was not a salesman at all, but one of the Antequera people seeing how I reacted to stress. So I said, 'No, of course. Go ahead.' I turned and faced the wall and off they went.

Of course, not all the tests were excruciating. Some even had what seemed to be some relevance to space travel.

In one they were checking our balance mechanisms, the vestibular canals in the ears. They would put hot water into an ear, or cold water, then swap over. Then they would look at our eyes. The effect of the temperature differential is that you feel dizzy and your eyes flicker. The doctors would measure how quickly our eyes stopped flickering and if one ear might have a different or more powerful effect than the other.

In another test they took us to a room with no visible light source, then made us walk on the spot with our eyes closed, lifting our feet up high with the back kept straight. Few people have both vestibular systems identical and, like all the others, I found I could not stop myself from moving off a bit to the side and forward a little. When I opened my eyes I was shocked to discover how far I had moved around. Quite a revelation!

Then, suddenly, we were finished. They told me I could go home and I did. I felt dazed and rather sore, but behind it all was a distinct feeling of having accomplished something. I moved around in a slight trance for a day or two, but almost without realizing it I was soon back to normal. Back at the Mars laboratory I found that I was a minor celebrity, which was not something I was looking for.

When I went to the hospital about my wisdom teeth I was told that all the three remaining ones should be extracted as a precaution, but that because of NHS waiting lists they wouldn't be able to do it for more than three months. As we were now at the end of September, this meant they couldn't be attended to until well after the decision. 'Of course,' said the consultant, 'if you were a *private* patient . . .'

I told him that through working for Mars I was in BUPA, and the modern miracle happened. I was admitted then and there, and all three teeth were removed that same afternoon.

That evening, sitting by myself on my bed, I took stock. The medical tests were still a recent memory, I had just had three large teeth removed under local anaesthetic, I had lost a lot of blood. I remember thinking, 'Shit! All this just to be an astronaut!'

The twenty-two were down to sixteen, and one of the other women had come through with me. We all lived too far away from each other for a coherent group to form, but by this time there was definitely a feeling of 'us against them', that we were going to get through this thing. I continued to be mildly famous at work and whenever I arrived in the morning I would usually be greeted with a list of phonecalls to return. One of the guys got so used to answering the phone for me that one day, in a particularly jocular moment, he picked up the receiver and said, 'Mission control.' This call happened to be from Peter Graham, the mission director at Antequera, who was not exactly amused.

We had been told that the final sixteen would soon be going down to the Institute of Aviation Medicine at Farnborough, but a day or so before these tests began I read something in a newspaper that I did not like at all.

It seemed that the Russians had said, of the candidates being tested in Britain, that they wanted the two finalists to be of the same sex. They expressed no preference about male over female, but the meaning was clear. With only two women left in the final sixteen, the odds against both of us beating all the men were negligible.

I brooded on this over the weekend, then on the Tuesday morning drove down to Farnborough to begin the tests. That day I cornered Peter Howard. I asked him straight out if the report was true. He looked at me in a serious way and confirmed it.

At that point I resigned myself to the fact that however well I might do, I was not going to get through. I had privately prepared a Plan B, though: I was now determined to enjoy myself while I was there.

Paradoxically, this apparently new Russian decision was one of the best things to happen to me since the selection began. I felt a great weight had been lifted and approached each of the new tests in the frame of mind that I wanted to see how far I could go and what my body would do. I began to think of the whole thing as a military assault course: tiring and difficult, but rewarding to be one of the ones who finished.

So far we had been tested exclusively by civilian doctors, but now we were being looked at by doctors who were in the RAF, specialists in aviation medicine. The atmosphere at Farnborough was purposeful and professional. It was actually the first time I had ever been on a military base and I was amazed by the difference between this and a civilian place.

A few of the remaining male candidates were in the forces, and some of them responded to the new environment with relish. I remember one of them said to me, intending perhaps to be sympathetic, 'It'll be pretty difficult for you, but of course I'm used to this kind of thing.' I remembered my earlier observations about how everyone except me already looked like an astronaut, and now the feeling was reinforced.

They tried to make us sick by putting us on a spinning chair. This is a fiendish device which rotates you while the instructor tells you to close your eyes and tip your head up and down from your knees to the head rest. After a few minutes of this most people feel at least disoriented and a little queasy.

Then there was the centrifuge, perhaps the centrepiece of the RAF's medical equipment at Farnborough. This consists of a small cage, which houses a seat and some other equipment, on the end of an arm that spins around inside a circular room. It looks like an attempt to cross-fertilize a fun-fair ride with a James Bond movie. It is used to simulate g-forces and the pressure on the body caused by acceleration or sharp changes in direction. The main problem with g-force is that the blood can be driven from the brain, depending on how you are orientated in the centrifuge, leading fairly quickly to a black-out. Some people are more resistant to this than others and the function of the centrifuge is to find out each individual's g-force tolerance. Air force pilots wear g-suits to help them cope with the effects of acceleration; these work by squeezing tightly on the legs and abdomen, thus helping to keep blood in the brain. We were being tested without g-suits because they wanted to see how our bodies would cope, so we were shown how to tense our muscles to have the same effect. They taught us how to hold our breath, and tense, then relax . . . and once this has been done a few times you can feel your blood pressure welling up.

I soon learnt how to control the g-forces in this way, and began to play with them. They told us that if we were on our way to blacking out, the first sign was a decrease in the amount of peripheral vision. It would seem as if a grey curtain were coming forward from each side of the head. They measured this by showing several coloured lights on a panel in front of our faces and we would respond by clicking a button when we saw certain of these appear. They therefore knew at any point the condition we were in and how we were coping.

The immediate reaction is to make yourself as tense as possible, but they told me to relax, not to make such hard work of it. As soon as I relaxed I could see the grey curtain, just as they had described. I found I could tense up and it would disappear; relax a little and it would sweep in again. I could play with it, make it go in and out!

There are other problems with the centrifuge at Farnborough. It's not a long arm, and because the machine is whizzing you around in a circle you're not just being pushed down into your seat, you're getting dizzy too. When the centrifuge stops, people who are prone to motion sickness feel as if they're tumbling and become physically sick. Some of the candidates were ill when it stopped.

When these tests were completed I went back to my job at Mars, and tried to get on with my work. It was extremely hard to do so. Quite apart from the media interest, which showed no sign of dying down, even the people at work were interested. I would go to a meeting, ostensibly to discuss some product, and inevitably someone would say, 'Tell us the latest!' The management remained totally cooperative. For a time they had guaranteed to give me a day off work for every day of my own holiday time, but when that was all used up they told me to carry on anyway. All on full pay!

A group of Russian doctors came to Britain to check the

current shortlist for themselves. They went through the medical and Farnborough results, and on the strength of those came up with a list of ten remaining candidates. I was the only woman and I assumed that my presence on the shortlist was now token. My main instinct, having come as far as this, was to see the thing through as far as possible, preferably to the end.

More medical tests! I went up to London for two days to meet the Russian doctors. My knowledge of the Russian language at this stage was still almost non-existent, but while I had been at Farnborough I had bought a Berlitz Russian course and had been playing it while driving to and fro in the car. This is not an ideal way to learn a language, but I at least knew how to count up to ten and how to say perhaps the most useful phrase of all, 'I do not understand.' Maybe it helped a little to be able to answer in rudimentary Russian: some of the eyesight tests involved identifying numerals buried inside a mass of coloured dots.

Whatever the reason, we were soon down to six of us: myself and five men. At this point the Russians revealed that they required IVPs (intravenous pyelograms) of the remaining candidates, but the BUPA clinic and NHS hospitals were refusing to carry out the procedure on fit patients. This threatened to be something of a stumbling block, as the Russians were adamant that a kidney check was essential, but in the end a private hospital was located where it could be done. The six of us were booked in for the following Thursday, 2 November.

Four months had elapsed since what I describe as the pivotal moment in my life. Although the demands of the Juno mission on my time had been intermittent, when they came they had been onerous and I had had to devote myself entirely to them. My days off work had been mounting and the actual work I had managed to do for Mars was negligible. All the way through these months I had kept firmly in mind that I was unlikely to be the one chosen, and I knew that if and when the peremptory rejection came I would have to make major amends to what must be one of the most cooperative employers in Britain. As well as the actual time I had given to the mission, the media circus had been growing steadily and indeed the ballyhoo showed every sign of being just about to take off. All this was a distraction; I felt my life had been knocked off course and that for a large part of those four months I had barely had a life outside the Juno mission.

As I entered the hospital appointment in my diary, I had little idea that my life from that moment would no longer be independent of the mission. Here is how the days went:

THURSDAY   *(2nd November 1989)*
I spent most of the day at the hospital having the IVP. Everything was said to be OK.

FRIDAY
Joanna Dodd, from the PR company Granard Rowland, telephoned me at Mars at 10.30 a.m., to ask if Independent Television News and Scottish TV could film me at work. Both of my managers were out. I had to go to one of the directors. He said immediately, 'Of course!' They cleaned out the lab and painted the walls white. The PR consultant arrived in the afternoon. Media people don't realize the chaos they cause . . . and if they do realize they don't care.

The STV crew arrived at about ten past four in the afternoon and didn't depart until after 7 p.m.! I tried to leave them to get on with it and did what I could to catch up on my work, but you can't pretend the presence of camera and lights is at all normal.

ITN took less time, presumably because their deadline was tighter. The ITN science correspondent persuaded me to answer a question as if I already knew the answer: 'Now, Helen, how do you feel now you've been chosen to be one of the final four?' I started to say, 'Well, I'm absolutely delighted, and, er—' But I couldn't go on. I added, 'Sorry, I'm not prepared to answer that question!' This was the first time I actually refused an answer to a journalist (and it would have to be to someone who, over the succeeding months in Russia, was to become a good friend and ally). Afterwards, the guys in the lab said, 'Well done, Helen. Don't take it lying down! Good on yer!'

Still no news from Antequera, though. It was the next day that I was expecting to hear the names of the final four. Was mine going to be one of them? If it was, I would have to get up to London to take part in the announcement on Sunday, but nobody was telling me anything. Yet again I felt immobilized. My job was plainly suffering, my parents were wondering why I hadn't been up to see them, Kevin, my boyfriend, had more or less given up hope of ever seeing me again and what about my Ph.D.?

I went home at last, and around 10.30 p.m. I went to bed. Peter Howard had not phoned: this was a significant negative. He had said, cryptically, that he wouldn't be able to tell us in advance who had been chosen, *but*, on this Friday evening, he would be making 'four telephone calls'. The inference I could make was clear: if I was going to be chosen he would ring me, but he wouldn't say anything about my being chosen! It was all academic, anyway, because the phone did not ring. Even cryptically.

SATURDAY

In the morning I was supposed to be giving an interview to the *Sunday Correspondent*, but I didn't want to get trapped into another of those 'How are you going to feel if you're chosen?' sessions. I rang Peter Howard to ask him if it was OK to do the interview. He told me that it would be fine and that I would be called later on to advise me whether or not I was in the final four. There was no explanation of why he hadn't telephoned the night before, or if, because of that, I was already out of the running without knowing it. I also wanted to know what was going on that evening, and would I have to go up to London or not?

At 4.20 p.m. I received a phonecall, telling me to be at Granard Rowland Communications that evening at 6 p.m. That was the entire message. Was I going up for the night? I had exactly an hour and forty minutes! I packed my bag, changed my clothes and left.

I arrived on time, but even so was the last of the four to get there. It seemed the final four had been decided, and it was going to be me, plus Tim Mace, Clive Smith and Gordon Brooks. I *was* delighted! But why couldn't they have told me properly, or even given me a bit more time? Obviously Gordon Brooks must have known for most of the day, as he had had to come up from Southampton. This was annoying me. Not for the first time, or indeed the last, I couldn't help thinking that all was not as it should be. Was this how NASA operated? Not a pleasant feeling. They gave us a dinner, then we all had to stay together in a hotel in London. We were under terrific conditions of secrecy. I wanted to ring my mum and dad and tell them the news, but that was strictly forbidden.

And the other two candidates, the ones who had gone through so much, who had passed test after test, who had suffered the same ragging of the media, who had gone through the painful and unethical IVP test? Out. Forgotten. Unmentioned. They had become non-people, as far as Antequera was concerned.

This Saturday night when I made it to the last four should have been a time of celebration. Instead, the furtiveness and PR-inspired attempts at 'secrecy' made all four of us uncertain and unhappy.

SUNDAY

I awoke at 6.30 a.m. and was immediately too wide awake to go back to sleep. By arrangement the night before, I met the three others for a quiet breakfast. This was my first real chance to get to know the other three. We all knew each other's names, and had seen each other from time to time during the selection process, but we had hardly had a chance to speak together. I already knew a little about Tim Mace, because we had happened to meet at the Brunel University weekend. Gordon Brooks was also in the military; he was a doctor in the Royal Navy and was a veteran of the Falklands War, during which his ship had been sunk. Of the four of us he was the only one who was married, and he had four children. Clive Smith turned out to live only a short distance away from me. He was working as a lecturer in Space Technology at Kingston Polytechnic (now Kingston University).

After breakfast we went to the Savoy, where a press conference had been arranged.

The big guns were assembling: I met Sir Geoffrey Pattie, director of the mission. While we were waiting for the conference to begin we were given a crude pep-talk by the PR agency, trying to hype us up into a performance. Consider the four of us, all engineers and scientists, one a doctor, one a lecturer: all mature professional people in their late twenties and thirties, unused to the limelight, more accustomed to cerebral work and private socializing. These dippy PR people were charging up and down, trying to wind us up. 'This is the BIGGEST MOMENT OF YOUR LIFE! You're going to go on stage, let's REHEARSE WALKING ON TO THE STAGE, come on, walk on as though you're proud to be on! Wow! It's a great day, THE PRESS ARE HERE!!'

I was thinking, 'I don't need this. I was fine before all this started happening. Now I'm nervous!'

Finally, in the spirit of going along with what we were told to do, we put a good face on it and strode confidently out on the stage to be presented. Whereupon the assembled press corps bombards us with . . . just one question: 'What has been the worst moment so far?' After all that build-up!

What we hadn't realized (and probably neither had the PR

people) was that journalists like to have their own interviews. After we had separated to do this for a while, we all trooped off outside for photos, which was great fun. I enjoyed that bit (a point I mention so I don't sound sour about the whole thing). Later I was photographed by *The Times*, and the next day my face was on the front page.

They kept up the pressure on us for most of the morning, the impact being the greater because of the suddenness with which we had been thrown into it. First we were told nothing, then we were expected to come up with an endless array of spontaneous answers for the press. Less than twenty-four hours earlier I had been wondering whether I should take the evening off and go and see Kevin, if he was still around, and now I was saturated with the attention.

There was a working lunch with the Mission officials and managers, followed by more interviews. I got away when I could and went straight home. The first thing I did when I went into my flat was pick up the phone and call my parents. They already knew the news, of course, having heard it on the BBC midday bulletin. Neighbours had been calling round all afternoon to see if they had heard.

I then rang Kevin, but he seemed to be out somewhere.

MONDAY
In the morning the car had a flat battery. I was about to go to Moscow and I couldn't start my car!

I went to the local newsagents, and for the first and only time in my life I bought a copy of every newspaper on the counter. I glanced through them all, partly interested, partly amused, but mostly recoiling in horror.

Today, for instance, gave potted descriptions of the four of us: Gordon Brooks was the 'Family Man', Clive Smith was the 'James Bond Lookalike', Tim Mace was the 'Officer and Gentleman', and I was the 'Token Woman'. That really riled me!

It wasn't so much that it was wrong, or offensive, or a distortion, or even that it had a grain of truth (although in minor ways it was all of these) . . . it was so unoriginal, so ham-fisted.

I finally got the car fixed and drove to Mars, where I found dozens of messages waiting for me. I spent all day returning the calls, or taking new ones. They were all from radio and press. I still saw myself as having only an outside chance and in my heart of hearts never thought I would be chosen. Even so, I was starting to think maybe there was a bit of a chance, if the stuff about two candidates of the same sex turned out to be wrong. I was just beginning to take myself seriously.

In between the interviews I was thinking about this. For instance, if I had actually thought when I first applied that I might be selected, I wonder if I would still have applied? If I had known what it was going to be like, maybe I would have thought it was too daunting a prospect.

Being strictly honest with myself, I knew that the fact I thought I wouldn't be chosen had made it easier to apply; even now, continuing to think of myself as the outsider made it easier to go on.

Time for more honesty in the evening, after I got home. I saw Kevin at last, and we had a long chat. A few weeks earlier, when I had been in the final thirty-two, I had asked him whether he would come to Russia with me if I was picked. At the time he had said no, but wanted to think about it. For most of the time since then he had been away, touring Europe on his own for six weeks. When he came back I was in the last ten and he said he had changed his mind and would go to Russia with me. By then, though, I had been through a rather strange time and, not being able to contact him while he was away, I had been forced to make my own decisions without considering anyone else. I had to tell him that I too had changed my mind, although I still didn't really expect to be chosen to go to Russia. However, now I was down to the final four and it seemed more possible than ever that I could be in the final two. We both knew if that happened it would be the end for us.

TUESDAY
Similar day to Monday. Piles of messages waiting for me when I got to the lab and long interviews all day. If anything it was not quite as intense as the day before, but it was still impossible to get any work done.

In the evening, went out for a Chinese meal with Kevin. Happened to see several management people from Mars and nearly didn't recognize them in their non-lab clothes.

WEDNESDAY
I had to be at Granard Rowland for an interview first thing in the morning. All four of the candidates were there; I bumped into Clive quite by accident at Surbiton station, and we travelled up together. The occasion was a fairly gruelling board interview with Juno management, in which we were interrogated closely about our motives for wanting to go into space and our attitudes to the various moral compromises we might have to make for the sake of sponsorship. These sort of questions are hard enough to deal with in the ordinary way, but as was always the case with Antequera, a certain extra something was added for piquancy. STV had their cameras in the room and filmed everything. Really disconcerting!

I felt afterwards that I had done particularly badly in this interview. I was reassured to discover that the other three felt much the same way, while none of us wanted to make excuses about the television crew being present.

Ironically, perhaps, in the afternoon they gave us a crash course on how to speak when on TV, how to deal with interviews and so on. This too was filmed by STV, creating Chinese boxes of meaning to the whole affair.

In the evening we all went to ITN (ITV were one of the Juno sponsors) for a reception. Later, we watched them broadcast the news.

I was home by about 10 p.m. and went straight to bed.

THURSDAY

I drove to Mars in the morning and made a conscientious effort to get some work done; I managed only ten minutes before the first interruption. I gave up after that.

At lunchtime, all my friends at Mars made me a going-away presentation. One of the guys had baked a cake with my picture on rice paper. There was a model of a rocket. They had bought me some thermal clothes, a suit carrier, some Russian books and cassettes. It was all very touching and bizarre, because I still hadn't been chosen to do any training; I was going away for a couple more weeks of medicals. I said to them, 'What happens if I want to come back? Will you mind?' Everyone was happy, but to me it was all a terrible wrench.

In the afternoon, the Mayor of Kingston wanted to see me and Clive Smith, so we went to his office and he gave us the Kingston flag and badge.

I had an hour or two of the afternoon left to myself and all sorts of little things needed doing. My car had to go in for a service. It was the first chance I'd had, so I dropped it off in Hampton and ran home (the only exercise I was able to get all week). I went to see my GP, and felt daft sitting in the waiting room in my running shorts.

FRIDAY

Another day off work, this time for the official Juno photographs, taken by Lord Snowdon. As soon as I arrived I realized not everything about the selection process was going to be bad. Snowdon had hired a 750 cc Kawasaki for the day and I posed in motorcycling leathers. Tim was in his parachute gear, Clive in his sports kit, and Gordon was wearing his diving suit. Snowdon took hundreds of pictures and we all had great fun. Overall, I felt it was a privilege to meet him.

Afterwards, back to Juno reality with a bit of a bump. It had been realized, a bit belatedly, that the four of us needed independent legal advice on the contracts of engagement we were being offered, so we went to see a solicitor, all paid for by Antequera. What I had thought in prospect would be a short meeting dragged on and on. We had still not finished by mid-evening, but the meeting broke up anyway. I finally left at about 10 p.m. and got home exhausted.

SATURDAY

I met Tim and his sister in Covent Garden, then went to the Adventure Shop where Clive and his girlfriend were waiting for us. We had been told we needed to kit ourselves out for two weeks in a Moscow winter and would need good coats, thermal underwear and warm boots. I spent a small fortune, then went home to pack.

SUNDAY

Heathrow Airport was the first item on the agenda. Kevin drove me there. The others arrived and we all checked in to an Aeroflot flight. Then: guess what? A last-minute photo opportunity under the Alcock and Brown statue. Just what we all wanted!

The plane was late departing, but we were at least all on board, actually setting off for Russia. I was tired after the long and hectic last few days, and because I'd set out from home without breakfast I was also ravenous. As the plane climbed out from Heathrow I wondered what Soviet airline food would be like.

Once we were airborne, the crew from STV reasserted themselves, smiling and familiar, their documentary about us still in progress. A microphone appeared, the camera started. It was time for an interview. I took a deep breath and replied to the first question. Unfortunately for STV (happily for me) our aircraft was making so much noise that the sound recordist couldn't pick up my words.

I pushed back my seat, closed my eyes, and slept.

5

6 DAYS OF WORLD PEACE

Mir – Home, Sweet Home

After the tense period while we docked with the space station, it was a relief to get back to the routines for which most of our training had prepared us. When we were certain that the electrical and hydraulic connections had been made and there was no possibility of an air leak, we equalized the pressures between us and the space station by opening a small valve used for this purpose. With this done we were able to remove our spacesuits.

Viktor[*] and Musa,[†] the two cosmonauts already aboard Mir, had been watching us through one of the space station windows as we docked, while keeping a watchful eye on their control displays. The space station is in the passive rôle during docking, so there was not much they could do, but Musa had taken some TV pictures.

Two hatches of course separate the craft immediately after docking, one on each side, and the one on the Soyuz is opened

[*] Viktor Mikhailovich Afanasyev. A Russian military pilot, Viktor was the commander of Soyuz TM–11, the spacecraft in which I was due to return to Earth. During the period I was on Mir Viktor was nominally in charge of the space station.

[†] Musa Khiromanovich Manarov, a civilian from Daghestan, on the Caspian Sea. Musa was the engineer on Soyuz TM–11. He and Viktor had been in space since the beginning of December 1990, when they were launched with Toyohiro Akiyama, the Japanese cosmonaut.

first. It's shaped like a large cone, carrying the whole docking mechanism, and it swivels right back into the orbital module. The alloy it was made from had been outside, directly exposed to the vacuum of space. As a consequence it smelt most unusual, perhaps best described as the sort of smell you associate with hot metal. In the normal way, in Earth's atmosphere, metal usually has a thin film of oxide on the surface, but with no oxygen outside and no pressure, this would have been removed.

The guys on the space station side then opened their hatch too and without much ceremony we just floated in. I was allowed to go first, as the guest. Viktor was waiting to greet us with bread and salt, the traditional Russian welcome. (Normally this is a fairly large 'cottage' type of loaf, with a depression in the top where they pour salt. You break off a bit of the bread, dip it into the salt and then eat it.) Viktor had taken a few pieces of bread out of the sealed packets, snapped some salt tablets and stuck them in the tops of the little bits of bread.

We hugged each other and moved around the station, with Musa filming most of it, and then went back and did it all over again! The point is that this meeting is all planned in advance and mission control wants to see it happening live. What they don't realize is that it's a personal moment: I had worked with Viktor and Musa before they went into space, they had become friends and we hadn't seen them for six months. None of us wanted to be on a live TV show, so once we had said our real hellos, we did it all a second time for the cameras.

My first impression of the space station itself was how large it was. We had of course worked in the simulator in Star City, but there were two main differences between that and the real thing. The first was that the simulator was in separate pieces, with only the small Kvant module bolted in place. The second was that being on the ground the effect of gravity made you orient towards the floor. In space, the freedom of three-dimensional movement makes even small areas (like the orbital capsule on Soyuz) feel larger.

DIAGRAM 3 – BASE BLOCK OF THE MIR ORBITAL STATION

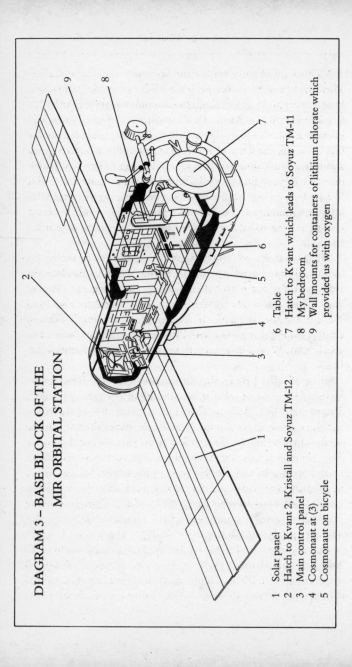

1 Solar panel
2 Hatch to Kvant 2, Kristall and Soyuz TM-12.
3 Main control panel
4 Cosmonaut at (3)
5 Cosmonaut on bicycle
6 Table
7 Hatch to Kvant which leads to Soyuz TM-11
8 My bedroom
9 Wall mounts for containers of lithium chlorate which provided us with oxygen

Another impression was of the immense amount of clutter! There had been an earlier problem with one of the unmanned Progress supply craft and about two tonnes of material had had to be taken aboard Mir. Most of it was still there, attached to the hull in every available space. The simulator had not prepared me for this. Even so, the sense of freedom and room in which to move about was miraculous. At first it was difficult to know in which direction to go to find the way around, but once again it was a bit like exploring a new home. All three of us were happy to be there, looking around, and I took many photographs with my own Olympus camera that I had taken to the station in the pocket of my spacesuit.

The first thing we were supposed to do was to move the biological experiments in from the Soyuz, and with that done we went back for our personal equipment, including the sleeping bags. Dinner that night had the novelty of being the first hot food we had had for two days. In the middle of the meal, mission control came through and said President Gorbachev wanted to speak to us. We felt it was worth breaking off from our meal for that!

Most of what I remember from those first few hours is the tremendous sense of relief at being there and of joining up with Viktor and Musa. Although there were certain things we had to get done (such as setting up some of the experiments), on the whole our schedule for the first few hours was relaxed. In this we were for once in agreement with the mission psychologists, who were keen for us to have this time to ourselves. So we drifted around in a fairly haphazard way, doing this and that. It was just so good to be free to do what we wanted to do, moving around the huge space station, staring out of the window and in the end staying up as late as we wanted.

One of the practical things I did on the first evening was to get to know the radio ham equipment. This was not one of the official experiments, but Richard Horton, a teacher at Harrogate Ladies' College, had a created a link-up with a number of schools in the

UK. I asked Musa to show me how the equipment was used, because over the last few months he had been making contact with operators all over the world.

The idea of the amateur radio contacts was that the children should work out how to track and contact a space station. They had to learn about orbits and radio technology in general, and in the process they learnt about organizing something which did not just involve themselves and their own school. It meant having to liaise with other schools and particularly other members of the community who often helped by providing the necessary equipment. Of course, we could only talk to them when our radio footprint was over Britain, which gave us maybe ten minutes or so. The real problem was the extra noise on the frequency, from so many other people who were trying to get through to the space station. On the whole British radio hams were good, in that they knew about the schools link-up and that they would be given their chance on the last day, so they tended to stay in 'listening mode'. As soon as the footprint crossed over into Europe, though, I was getting so many signals that they drowned out the schools. Although the people on Earth could hear me, it was frustrating because I couldn't hear what the children were asking me. I did catch a few of the questions and some more in enough bits from which I was able to make up an answer, but eventually I decided the best thing to do was to give a running commentary on what it was like to be in space, what I would be doing on the station, what I could see from the window and so on. It turned out they could hear this clearly.

Towards the end of the day we watched our docking on the videotape Musa had made, but after that we were all tired. At about 2 a.m. we all went to bed.

They let me use one of the two bedrooms (a small vertical space in the base block about the size of a broom cupboard, which in the weightless state meant it was easily big enough; it had its own window), while Viktor used the one opposite. Musa had made his own sleeping area in the Kristall module. Sergei and Tolya put their sleeping bags wherever there happened to be some spare room. Sleeping bags had to be tied 'down' to stop them floating away. Due to the circulation of air around the station provided by the fans, if the bags were not fastened to something they too, with their occupants, would circulate around the station.

I wrote up my diary before falling asleep. 'Ace evening,' is what I said.

We had launched on Saturday and now it was the following Tuesday, my first full working day on Mir. I was due to return to Earth at the weekend. Time suddenly felt short.

I started the day by removing the braslets from the tops of my legs. They were so uncomfortable to wear that I decided whatever disadvantages there were to taking them off could not be much worse than leaving them on.

I wanted to use a camera and knew there were several on the station, so I went around looking for one. There was so much rubbish aboard it was difficult finding anything and the first couple of cameras I came across already had film inside them. I eventually managed to commandeer a Nikon, as well as an old Video-8. I located another of the experiments (a biochemical blood test) and made sure it was ready for use. I also got going on the electrotopographic experiment, a study of materials and coatings made by this process. There were trivial problems associated with most of the experiments: some of them had been sent up in separate parts, for instance, and I had to locate them all before I could begin. In another experiment, the growing of seedlings, I had to find a part of the space station which had a suitable light source.

The high point of the day for the British press was an advertisement I had to broadcast for Interflora, one of the sponsors of the mission. The idea was that I would romantically order flowers for someone on Earth and be televised doing so. I was happy to oblige, but the idea, although not specified, was obviously that I should send some flowers to a lover. I could easily imagine the reactions of the tabloid press to this (and the upheavals that would follow in the life of the hapless recipient), so I sent some roses and freesias to my mum. I knew it would disappoint the press but she was actually the one to whom I wanted to send flowers.

In the afternoon I managed to link up with one of the schools in the radio scheme and later with GB0JUNO, Harrogate Ladies' College, but again there was a lot of background noise and contact was erratic.

That night we planned to have our one celebratory meal, all of us present at once, concentrating on nothing but the pleasure of each other's company. I decided this was the occasion on which to bring out Leonov's chiffon dream-garment. As I floated back into the base block towards the others there were a few exclamations and a short round of applause. Then Sergei remembered that he too had a surprise for us. He had brought up a tie to wear for dinner, which duly floated horizontally the whole evening!

The food was quite palatable, although of course very Russian, and for eight days there was plenty of variety. We ate from tins containing fish or meat and potatoes, and from tubes containing soft cheese. There were packets of dried soup, vegetable purée and kasha (a grain similar to oats) that we reconstituted with hot water, and we snacked on nuts, tiny portions of black bread and dried fruit. Our spoons and forks (no knives officially allowed) were equipped with holes at the end of the handles for thread to tie them to the table. We drank water from the pressurized container, sweet coffee and tea from plastic packets with spouts to roll out and suck through, and fruit juice from tubes whose caps were attached by pieces of string thoughtfully provided by the ground staff.

We were halfway through the meal, with the space station

passing through the shadow of the Earth, when the emergency signal sounded. This signal has two modes. The first is a constant beep, which broadly means: General Warning. Our usual response to this would be to move over to the control panel to find out what was going on and take action if necessary. The second mode is an insistent series of short beeps, indicating that this is more than a warning and that something needs to be done immediately. On this occasion there was a series of beeps.

Viktor went down to the control panel immediately, then came back to say that the batteries were low. It had happened on occasion before and in itself was not too worrying, even though there was nothing we could do about it. All we had to do was wait until the space station moved out into the sunlight again, whereupon the solar panels would start generating electricity. For several weeks there had been a problem with the computer that orientated the panels in order to receive maximum energy from the sun and this was why we had brought up a replacement computer.

A few moments after the alarm the ventilating fans began to slow down, then came to a halt. The noise of these fans is a constant feature of life aboard Mir. Twenty-four hours a day they recirculate the air, allowing it to dehumidify as far as possible, filter out a lot of the dust and debris, be cleaned of unwanted substances, such as ammonia, carbon monoxide and carbon dioxide. The fans make an appreciable racket, and they are something you quickly have to get used to. The first fans to stop were those at the extremities of the station, in the Kristall and two Kvant modules; shortly afterwards, the fans in the base block slowed down, then halted. From being a noisy place, the space station became silent. After the fans, the lights extinguished themselves, again starting from the outer modules. When the lights in the base block failed, all we were left with was a solitary emergency fluorescent tube.

It felt, unmistakably, as if the station had started to die and it gave me a cold, sinking feeling. It was not fear, because this was one of the many eventualities for which we had been trained, so we knew exactly what was happening and why; it was more a sense of identity with the space station itself, that its life was vulnerable. For a few more minutes we were helpless, drifting in space in what had suddenly become a lifeless hulk.

Then the sun reappeared over the horizon.

We all woke late the next morning. According to our schedule of work we were supposed to have breakfast first thing, followed by experiments, but to catch up I did some experimental work as soon as I was up. Breakfast was fitted in later, as and when I could grab a few bites. In general, we found the schedule rather restrictive; it seemed to be designed as a régime that ensured everything would be done, rather than as a practical way of actually getting it done. What people on the ground always overlook is the fact that astronauts are highly motivated and enjoy their jobs! While I was on the space station we all rather took the line that so long as we got the experimental and technical work done, it should not matter to mission control when and how we did it.

During my whole time on the station relationships between the five of us were excellent. We had a great sense of unity, of being a team. I imagine that it is not always so, that people being people, there must be times when irritation or arguments take over, but while I was in space there was no hint of this. It was of course a fairly unusual time, with five astronauts in the space station instead of the usual two, and one of them British and a woman to boot. Discounting all of this, it was a crew changeover period, with two of the men looking forward to getting back to Earth, the other two anticipating a long stay and with many particular bits of information for the old crew to pass on. I was not involved in most of this.

Another of the sponsors was a computer manufacturer called Poqet Computers, and I had to be photographed using one of their ingenious hand-held machines. I was pleased to do so and did it with cheerful countenance.

Generally the next four days were when I carried out most of the work to which I had been assigned, done at the relaxed pace in weightlessness that is such an easy and pleasant habit to pick up. I spent long periods at the window, watching the Earth and photographing it. I returned to the electrotopographic experiment, exposing certain films to the vacuum and radiation of space. I started the Prognos experiment, and later tried unsuccessfully to get Musa interested in doing some of the biological experiments with me. In the evening I helped Viktor with stamping some of the first-day covers.

I never felt imperilled on Mir, even during that time when the lights went out. The longer I stayed aboard the more at home I felt, and therefore the safer I felt. The mission psychologists might have something to say about this, but for me it was partly the product of the intensive training, which prepared me for the reality of the station, and partly the calibre of the other crew members.

To a large extent I was supposed to leave the running of the station to the others, even though I had been trained to know and understand Mir's layout and functions. I had been taught, for instance, what was to be found behind every single panel and access door, so that if something had been urgently needed I would have been as capable of getting hold of it as any of the others. I could even have operated the space station's main controls. I also had to know the drills in case of emergencies: fire, of course, and (in space, much more likely) meteor strike. I had to know which fire extinguishers to use, where they were and how to use them; also how to isolate certain parts of the station, turn off the ventilation, close hatches and if necessary evacuate. We had gas masks available. One of the things we had to practise was how to put on a gas mask while wearing a spacesuit. This, I can say with certainty, is not an easy thing to do.

The day-to-day activities of keeping the station up and running, though, were among the jobs Sergei and Tolya had been intensively trained for, so for me there had not been a great deal of emphasis on this. All I had to know was what to do if the others were not able to do it themselves. As I say, I was happy to leave it to them and at no point did I feel in danger.

On the Thursday morning we reset the alarm to wake us up moments before my first commitment. I therefore went almost straight from my sleeping bag to a live appearance on TV-AM; no matter how far you travel, it seems, there is no escape from breakfast TV! Later that day there were more press conferences and I managed to make radio contact with some of the schools in Britain. By the end of that day I was convinced that living and working in a state of weightlessness was completely natural and instinctive.

Friday and Saturday were my last two complete days on the station, and I knew I was trying to make the most of the experience, valuing every moment I was awake and rather resenting the hours when I had to sleep. I concluded the experiments and prepared what results I could for the return. I made my last radio calls to the schools in Britain. A piece at a time we started packing. Thoughts were dominated more and more by the unwelcome prospect of the return to Earth.

I found myself drawn more frequently to the windows, spending longer periods of time there. Sergei and Tolya were busy preparing themselves for their long stay, while Viktor and Musa were readying themselves more prosaically for the onslaught of gravity on their long-weightless bodies. Meanwhile, I stared wistfully at the world to which I was soon to return, running film after film through the cameras, trying to capture and preserve for ever these haunting images of the glorious Earth outside.

6

4 TO 2

Selection for Training

Gordon Brooks, Clive Smith, Tim Mace and myself landed at Moscow Airport, still more than slightly worn out after the last hectic week in London. We were met by two people, one of whom was one of the doctors who would be looking at us, the other from NPO Energia, a part of the Soviet space agency. They led us through customs. Waiting for us in the main hall of the airport were ITN. The reporter stepped forward. 'How do you feel now, to be in Moscow?' Maybe it was their way of making us feel at home . . .

Outside the airport we were conducted to the bus which had been laid on for us. While in Moscow we rarely travelled in cars, at least when being taken around officially. The buses were supposed to be safer. Once you had seen the perilous way in which most Soviet cars were driven, you began to realize they might be right. In a pile-up, at least you would probably be in the bigger vehicle. The weather, as we drove from the airport, was dark and unsettled, with sleet in the wind. We barely gained an impression of Moscow, partly because it was almost nighttime as we arrived and partly because we didn't see the centre of the city. We headed out to the north-west on a wide dual carriageway, lined with big modern blocks of flats.

We reached the hospital uneventfully about twenty minutes

later and were given a most gratifyingly warm welcome by the
staff. One of the ENT doctors, who told us to call her Ludmilla,
did most of the talking and showed us where we would eat and
where we would be sleeping. All this was translated for us by
Barbara Zielinska, an interpreter employed by Antequera, who
had been on the flight with us. We were glad she was there,
because our collective knowledge of Russian remained a notch
or two above zero.

We had been allocated a small wing of Hospital No. 6 (the
official name); Clive and I were each given a largish room
with a bathroom, while Tim and Gordon shared. There was
also a communal room for us. They had gone to some trouble
to make the rooms pleasant, but there was no mistaking that
we were in a hospital: there was for instance an oxygen supply
beside each bed. It was the first time in my life I had ever had
to sleep in a hospital. I was touched that they had thought to
lay out some blue-and-white-striped flannel pyjamas for us,
but slightly amused by the thought that I was seriously
intended to use them. (They were enormous. One size fits all
male Russians! The bottoms felt as though I had a whole sheet
curled around each leg; I could have cut them in half and used
one leg as a nightdress! In the end I compromised by sleeping
in the top half only.)

There was nothing for us to do on that first evening. We
unpacked, then ate the supper the hospital provided for us. We
all felt extremely warm, even uncomfortably warm, and
stripped down to T-shirts. The nurses were worried by this,
thinking we would catch colds. Russians like to keep their
buildings much warmer than we are used to: the average
centrally heated British house would have most Russians
reaching for an extra pullover or two. On the whole, though, we
were all glad to be there. At last we were doing something and it
would be fair to say we were all a little excited. Maybe this was
why, when my blood pressure was unexpectedly measured at
bedtime, it was found to be a little high.

★

Blood pressure, pulse and temperature were taken again in the morning, before I was allowed out of bed. I peered at the results: still a little high. I wasn't used to this!

After breakfast (corn and dumpling, with cheese, bread and biscuits, all very sweet) we waited for something to happen. Nothing happened. Nobody told us anything. Had people forgotten we were here?

Towards the end of the morning Peter Howard, Barbara Zielinska and another mission doctor called James Witchalls dropped in to see us. We leapt excitedly to our feet. They looked around at our rooms, checked everything was all right, satisfied themselves there was nothing going on, then departed to their hotel. We sat down again.

Lunch was another solid, starchy meal. In our normal lives all four of us were physically active people and for a whole day we had been doing almost nothing except sitting around and eating. We took matters into our own hands and went for a run in the grounds. It was cold and damp outside and some of the ordinary patients from the hospital, who were just walking around sensibly, looked at us as if we were crazy. Apparently, few people run for recreation in Moscow. In the end it was more of a gesture than anything else, because the hospital grounds were fairly restricted in extent. Afterwards, we showered, then watched TV. Boredom continued.

After another hefty dinner they again took our blood pressure; mine was still high and we started feeling slightly concerned. Why should this be so? One of the nurses made me lie down for an hour to see if my blood pressure would drop a bit. It did.

The best thing that happened that day was something else that *didn't* happen: no reporters, no Scottish TV, no ITN. Bliss! It was our first day free of all that for ages. Why hadn't they been pestering us? Could it be because they, unlike us, knew all along that nothing was going to happen?

The next morning it started to snow and this time it seemed to be settling on the ground. At last the grey, monolithic view from the hospital windows began to look a little like we had imagined Russia might be.

After breakfast they took some blood samples from our fingers and while this was still going on a lot of doctors arrived. Then Peter Howard, James Witchalls and Barbara Zielinska turned up. We were pleased by all this; it felt as if something were at last about to start happening. Even so, we couldn't help feeling a little jealous when we noticed James had bought himself a coypu hat; this must have meant that they had been out shopping the day before. Maybe this obsession with our freedom now seems petty, but it was a result partly of being stuck uselessly in an institution where none of us spoke the language and partly a growing realization that it seemed to be the mission director's policy to keep us out of touch with the outside world. This situation was to grow much more noticeable over the next few days.

Peter Howard had lunch with us that day, but he was in a dismal, uncommunicative mood. There was obviously something on his mind that he was not able to tell us. Naturally, this made us more curious, but little was forthcoming. How could it be anything that did not, in some way, affect us? However, vague hints started to slip through as the meal progressed. According to Peter, it seemed that the Russians had thought they were taking on four fit and healthy people, suitable for the job, but now they were complaining that small things were wrong with us.

Naturally, we were for a time somewhat downcast by his mood, but once he had gone we came to the conclusion he was simply misunderstanding what was going on. We had already started to grasp how the Soviet bureaucracy worked: at every level people had to justify their existence, so a medical examination was virtually guaranteed to throw up every tiny aberrant detail, just in case the results were compared with someone else's.

By about 4.30 p.m. the Soviet doctors had decided what extra tests they wanted to do on us and they all left. We went for a walk in the grounds, beginning to feel much more united. We were starting to get to know each other, joining up, sensing that it was the four of us against the rest of the world. We had a snowball fight.

Afterwards, back in Building No. 3, Hospital No. 6, we returned to our boring routine. We had a little nap before dinner, then watched TV, then read for a while. A casual comment from one of us opened up a whole new subject of concern: we were all finding the Russian language difficult to learn and only now were beginning to realize the sheer scale of what we had taken on.

The next morning, after our now-routine blood pressure tests, and after the most extraordinary breakfast of spam, peas and semolina, we were taken by minibus to another hospital, one which was specifically for testing pilots. Immediately, our interest quotient rose, although it sagged somewhat when we were given hearing and ENT tests *yet again*! Afterwards we were tested on the altogether more relevant tilt table, on which one is strapped in a horizontal position while the whole thing is tilted to various angles to the horizontal, many of them involving the head being held lower than the rest of the body.

While we were still being tested, a team from Moscow television turned up and filmed us for a show called *Man, Earth and the Universe*. In a rather touching reversal of the usual rôles on TV, the presenter was more nervous than us! Whatever the reason, she took the trouble to interview us in English, a courtesy we all appreciated.

At lunchtime we returned to our hospital; afterwards we were given some psychological tests. We tried to enter into the spirit of the thing, because after all this had so far been our most interesting day to date. First was a colour test. The psychologist gave us six cards each and told us to sort them out into our favourite order. When we had done this she asked us to do it

again and we obliged. At this point she complained that we had
put them in the same order as before. Apparently, most of the
people she tested got muddled up and put them in a different
order.

From this we moved to a questionnaire, thankfully in English.
It was absolutely vast, consisting of 566 questions on loosely
psychological subjects, such as our sex-lives and what we
thought of our respective mothers. The hospital only had one
copy of the questionnaire, so we had to take it in turns. It took
about two hours to answer all the questions and, glad of the
diversion, I settled down to do it first. All sorts of internal
evidence, such as the spelling, indicated that the test had
originated in the USA, and according to a copyright notice at the
end had been compiled in 1943. What it was doing, nearly half a
century later, in a hospital in Moscow was something we found
rather distracting. It was of course hopelessly out of date, but in
addition it made cultural assumptions that completely baffled us.
For instance, one question asked: 'Did you enjoy playing "Drop
the Handkerchief"?' Answering yes or no to this seemed
distinctly hazardous in what it might reveal! I went to the
psychologist and told her there were several questions I didn't
understand. She said, locked within the inscrutability of her
profession, 'Ah! We are not prepared to explain. Just answer in
the way you feel best.' I have often wondered since what the
Russian psychologists made of our results.

As a distraction it rated not all that high and did not last long.
When the evening came we were still as bored as ever. We left
the television on while we were eating dinner. President
Gorbachev was speaking; he must have gone on for more than
two hours. Later, Gordon found some dominoes in a cupboard
and we leapt on them with demented relief. We used some
kopeks left by Peter Howard for points: the process of being
institutionalized was now almost complete. We had no roubles;
we did not need money. Everything was taken care of.

★

The next day, however, was the one we had been looking forward to. We all woke early and dressed in our Juno tracksuits, because we were going to Star City.

The bus skirted around Moscow, following a number of dual carriageways. There was a huge amount of traffic, nearly all of which was heavy lorries. There seemed to be many more trucks than you would see in Britain, all painted a mid-blue or dark-green colour, transporting huge things, like whole prefabricated roofs. The snow was thick on the ground, but the roads had been gritted so that the sides were slushy. The cars we saw were filthy!*

While the road still ran close to Moscow it was lined with the huge, drab concrete apartment blocks I had seen earlier, but as the bus went further out we saw many lovely traditional wooden houses built along the side of the road. Quite unlike the flats, they were painted in gay colours and adorned with intricate wood carvings. Life in them looked as if it was fairly primitive: we couldn't help noticing there were water hand-pumps every few hundred metres. We could smell woodsmoke.

As you reach Star City there is a big field on the left, in an area called Bear Lake, and on the far side of this we could see several large satellite dishes, used for tracking the space station.

Star City is a modern, purpose-built town of about 4,000 people, a kind of combination university campus, suburban town and military training camp. Most Soviet cosmonauts live and train there (a few, the civilian cosmonauts, live in Moscow), as well as all the instructors, administrators and mission planners. By Soviet standards, the people who live there, which

---

* Moscow is the dirtiest city I've ever been in. After a couple of days on the ground the snow goes black. A few months later I discovered that in summer Moscow is dusty and sooty, but as soon as the weather turns cold it becomes wet, slushy and dirty. When I eventually had the use of a car I would sometimes drive into Moscow, an hour from Star City. Before driving back I would have to clean the headlights because otherwise the build-up of dirt was so thick they wouldn't be able to light the road in front of me.

include the families of the cosmonauts, have a reasonably privileged and comfortable existence. Under normal circumstances, at that time, Star City was one of those places in the Soviet Union closed to foreigners, unless on an organized tourist day-trip from Moscow.

Although we were greeted, and to a large extent treated, like VIPs in Star City, we were there to go through a few more tests. While our hangers-on, the mission managers, the journalists, were led away for coffee and chocolate, we had to get down to business. We all had to go through vestibular tests (the spinning chair again, with its attempts to make us feel sick), while Clive had to go on the centrifuge to repeat some tests he had taken at Farnborough, when there had been poor connection on one of his electrodes. It was also an opportunity for the Soviet space doctors to get a baseline on one of us. It took ages to wire up Clive for the test and we all felt sorry for him, mainly because the press were crowding around him and to at least some extent treating it as if he had failed the earlier test.

At last I was starting to feel that we were *really there*, that this was the real thing.

After lunch (virtually a banquet, with much cognac and champagne, and a considerable number of toasts) we walked around Star City and saw some of the monuments, notably Gagarin's. Everything was on a huge scale, something I was learning to identify as uniquely Soviet. Back in the buildings, we saw the mock-up of Mir (although only from the outside), were shown some spacesuits and went to inspect the hydro pool, where they practise their spacewalks. We also saw their planetarium, of which they're justifiably proud. When the bus took us back to the hospital we were sorry to leave.

In the evening, Clive essayed the 566 questions on the test form. Perhaps because we had been allowed out for a treat (or, more charitably, perhaps because she wanted to go home), the nurse in charge asked us to go to bed at 10 p.m. There was nothing much on TV we wanted to watch that night, so we agreed.

Two more days passed slowly. Every now and then one or another of us would be pulled out for another medical check, but for most of the time we felt useless and inactive. On the Sunday, a week after our arrival, the nurses mentioned that an 'English TV crew' wanted to see us. We rushed down to reception, eager for any distraction, even an interview!

It was ITN. They thought they were there to do a short interview, while we saw their presence as a way of escape. We walked straight past the nurses in reception, indicating we would be back later, and then out; out of the hospital grounds and into real, live Moscow. ITN took a short film of us going down the road to a lake, and then STV arrived with a bus. All of a sudden and, it seemed, for the first time, the media were on our side! We let them drive us into the centre of the city and at last we did some sightseeing. We saw the Kremlin. St Basil's Cathedral. Red Square. The Tomb of the Unknown Soldier. We saw the changing of the guard outside Lenin's Mausoleum. Gladly, graciously, we let the TV crews film as much as they wished. They took us to the Exhibition of Economic Achievements, which is a fairly large open area close to the centre of the city where a number of exhibition halls have been built. The one we all wanted to see was the space museum. Here were life-sized models of early space-craft, the original Sputnik, more recent Soyuz craft and so on . . . as well as a huge mock-up of the Soyuz/Apollo spacecraft joined together.*

By 3 p.m. we were all cold and tired and feeling we had been out in the streets too long. The reality, perhaps, was that

---

* Since the collapse of the Soviet Union there has been a certain downgrad-ing of public pride in the Soviet space achievements. The space museum is still there, but bizarrely the floorspace is now used as a secondhand car salesroom.

we had been quartered too long in overheated buildings, but the effect was the same. STV took us to one of the cooperative restaurants in Moscow for a late lunch.

We returned to the hospital feeling like errant children. The nurses were displeased with us and let us know it. At first we reacted a little defiantly, but gradually the story came out. We were their responsibility; if anything happened to us, they would suffer. Their biggest worry was that we would get ill and it was not without foundation. We learnt that when the Japanese team had been at the hospital, doing exactly the same as us, they too had been out to a restaurant and one of them had come down with food poisoning. It was clear that if they had known in advance what we wanted to do the nurses would not have allowed us to go.

Somewhat chastened, we spent a quiet evening. The nurses' worry was another small example of the differences between our cultures. Russians instinctively accept a need-to-know basis; the fact that someone tells them what to do or what not to do is in itself usually a good enough reason for doing or not doing it. In the West, of course, we like to know as much of the whole picture as possible so we can make up our own minds.

I was to run across this difference later, during the training, but eventually I worked out how to deal with it. I realized that the person who was telling me what to do knew no more than I did about why I should do it. It just had to be done and I was happy to accept that, because that was itself the system. There was no use fighting against it. After all, I hadn't come to any harm yet. Not physically, anyway.

Another two days dragged by, while our boredom and frustration grew apace. On the Tuesday morning I was getting ready to go out for a run in the grounds when one of the nurses stopped me. She needed to take a blood sample.

There followed a minor but disturbing incident. She wanted

to take blood from a vein, but they had no syringes. She produced instead a rather large, rather blunt reusable needle. She stuck this in my arm, then held a test tube underneath the open end while the blood trickled in. When that tube was full it was neatly swapped for another. At the time HIV was officially non-existent in the Soviet Union, which was about the most comfort I could draw. I saw it as yet another in the endless series of discomforts and risks I was having to suffer for the sake of being a cosmonaut.

Peter Howard and Barbara Zielinska turned up at the hospital that morning. We took the opportunity to vent some of the frustration we were feeling, in particular the now acute sense that we were being denied access to the outside world. All four of us had reasons for wanting to speak to family and friends at home, and anyway we wanted to know what was going on in the world. No phonecalls home were allowed, though. Why? Because Peter Howard said so.*

Quite apart from personal matters, we had some Antequera business to complete. We still had not been able to finalize the contracts they wanted us to sign and now Peter Graham, the mission director, turned up in Moscow with the latest version of the text. We were nervous of signing because we knew that two of us would be training in the Soviet Union, and two of us would be in reserve in the UK, but at this stage we had no idea which of us would be doing what. It seemed to us that committing ourselves at this moment might adversely affect the position of the two who were in reserve. None of us liked this feeling. After we had read through the contracts we decided that because we were now under considerable pressure to sign we needed to talk to the lawyer, and more urgently than ever.

---

* The Berlin Wall had fallen on 10 November 1989, two days before we arrived in the Soviet Union. Since then, the Communist leader of Bulgaria had resigned, riots had flared up in the Moldavian Soviet Republic and Czechoslovakia was in the grip of pro-democracy demonstrations. As far as we were concerned it could all be happening on another planet.

Peter Graham called back that evening to confirm that we were incommunicado and not allowed to make calls to Britain. He offered to pass on any message we cared to send.

Another matter that was beginning to rankle was that we had learned that our families were already being contacted, without our permission. This was starting to get out of control, and was not fair. If we wanted our families involved in PR stunts that should be our decision, not that of outsiders. The point was that by this time all our families must have been wondering why they hadn't heard from us and would be eager to hear from anyone. We already knew how unscrupulous the press could be. If someone rang my parents, say, and asked them to take part in a film, they would naturally assume that I knew about it and had agreed to it and would therefore feel pressurized to say yes.

In the evening Joanna Dodd, from the PR company, came over to brief us on what was going to happen during Saturday's television show. This was the one where the two who would go for training would be announced and Joanna's announcement was the first we had heard of it. We were all highly sceptical. Another televised stunt seemed inevitable. Joanna tried to reassure us, saying it would be held at the Science Museum, that it would be low-key and scientific. We suspended judgement, knowing we were anyway helpless to influence events.

Of much more immediate importance was the meeting of the State Commission, when the Soviet doctors would pronounce their verdicts on our suitability. We began to dress and prepare for it leisurely, because they had told us it would not begin until 11 a.m. At 9.30 a.m. someone rushed in to say it was going to begin in twenty minutes! We were taken over to another building, suddenly feeling hurried and flustered. STV and ITN were already there, as was everyone else, so *they* had known what time it was going to begin.

The building was buzzing with activity, with high-ranking doctors and medical teams visible on all sides. Some of the people were in uniform and we saw medals galore. They formed themselves into a number of smaller groups and dispersed to several consulting rooms. The four of us were conducted from one group to the next, where, once again, we were prodded in all the usual places and peered at minutely. All the doctors carried out the same tests. Everyone had to be satisfied!

When it was over they all assembled in a big room and a major discussion began. We could hear vague muffled sounds from the anteroom where we were waiting, but all we could do was sit tight.

At last some kind of consensus must have been reached, and they asked us to enter the room one by one, be presented to the Chairman of the State Commission, then listen to the verdicts. I went first. The chairman, a large and jovial man in a military uniform, said, 'Helen Sharman has been approved for training without reservation.' Everyone clapped and I went to a seat in the audience.

Then it was Tim Mace's turn. He was brought in and told that he too was fit for training. Clive was next and was told that his tonsils needed to be removed, whereafter he too would be fit. Finally, Gordon. There was a similar problem for Gordon, but they added that after removal of his tonsils he was also likely to be fit for training. Gordon put a brave face on it, but I knew that he was disappointed. This subtle distinction was clearly enough to put him out of the running and he knew it at once.

That night we were allowed out to eat in a restaurant, I suppose because whatever harm might befall us could no longer be blamed on anyone. Many of the people from Antequera were there, including the man who was responsible for the marketing. Everyone from the mission now seemed to be out here in Moscow and it felt as if a lot of things had been going on while we were incommunicado. Now we were all together again, part of the team once more. They were talking to us openly, treating us to a huge and expensive meal; it was almost as if they were saying sorry for having been so shitty for the last week. Even the outstanding matter of the contracts no longer appeared to be an issue. When one of us tentatively raised the sore point, Peter Graham said, 'Oh, we're not too desperate about you signing that. Don't worry about it!'

After a late night, we woke up the next morning to await further instructions about what we were required to do. Unexpectedly, and infuriatingly, it seemed we were going to have to kick our heels in the hospital for another full day.

At lunchtime the lawyer telephoned from London and we sorted out a few minor points about the contracts, but we agreed that we would make personal contact with him as soon as we were back in England.

The idleness gave us time to ponder the meaning of the decisions the day before and, although we didn't say too much between ourselves, we were obviously still in broad agreement. Gordon, for instance, was apparently now resigned to the fact he was not going to be selected. Too much doubt had been placed over him. Clive, though, remained optimistic, as did Tim and I.

Officially, the final decision was to be made in Britain, by the Juno management, the directors of Antequera; the Russian contribution had been merely to confirm that medically we were all suitable for training. If the unofficial reality was any different from this I've no idea what it might be. All I know is that by this stage the four of us felt like lumps of flesh whose main function was to be prodded, moved about and potentially discarded.

After much effort, in the afternoon of this last day, Clive managed to set up a meeting with a couple of the Russian friends he had made earlier that year at a meeting in Strasbourg of the International Space University. They gave us a guided tour of Moscow, as seen through eyes like our own. We used the Metro, experienced Moscow driving at first hand, even had tea at one of their homes. For a few hours we forgot about doctors, journalists and space missions. This was freedom!

In the evening we were invited out to dinner by Russian friends of Cathy Judelson, one of the interpreters. Once again, we found ordinary Soviet citizens to be exceedingly hospitable and friendly, and displaying many acts of generosity. We were welcomed with open arms into a flat that must have been cramped even without us, and were given a huge Georgian-style dinner, washed down with plenty of Georgian cognac. That one meal probably cost that family most of a month's wages. When we finally got back to the hospital, one of the nurses came down to let us in, wearing her nightclothes. She was much more relaxed than before the State Commission and seemed genuinely pleased that we had been enjoying ourselves.

At 11.30 a.m. the next day Ludmilla ushered us into the dining room and the doctors and nurses gave a little party for us. We realized at this point that they had all become rather attached to us. Quite a few misty eyes! It was as if we had come through something together. We exchanged what gifts we could: we all gave away our Juno T-shirts, and Clive's notably thoughtful girlfriend Cornelia had given him some make-up and tights to bring with him. My mum had given me some brand-new knickers and a bar of soap, which I hadn't yet opened, so I passed these on to highly appreciative recipients. Just as we were about to leave, one of the nurses gave me a ring of her own. We all departed feeling tearful and unexpectedly emotional.

From the hospital we went to the British Embassy. At short notice the ambassador and his wife had laid on a lunch for us and invited some officials from Star City. I was seated between Major-General Djanibekov, in charge of all the academic training at Star City, and the ambassador. Afterwards, all the ITN people gathered in the hall to say goodbye. Emotions began to run high again.

The British Embassy had provided a minibus to get us to the airport, but first we all wanted to go to GUM. We were still more or less without a supply of roubles, but Barbara gave us some of hers. I saw some coat-hooks in the shape of painted bears I thought I'd like as a souvenir. Russian shops operate a weird and discouraging system of payment. First of all you have to clamour around the counter with everyone else, catch the assistant's eye, then point out what you want to buy. The assistant gives you a written slip of paper, which you take to a cashier's desk. After an immense wait in a queue, you pay over the money, then take the receipt back to the counter. If the goods you wanted are still there (sometimes they vanish during the wait in the queue) the assistant lets you have them.

GUM, more an arcade than a department store (which is how it is often described in the West), seemed to be full of shoe shops. We all commented on this. Much later, when I had been living in the Soviet Union for some time, I realized that what happens is that while shoes are available they sell shoes. The shops will then be empty for a while, until a consignment of (say) jackets arrives from somewhere like Czechoslovakia; at this point, the clothes shops fill up with and sell jackets.

We walked back through Red Square to the bus. By now it was just about getting dark and snow was falling. They were big snowflakes, falling quietly on a windless evening, lit by the streetlights, drifting through the beams of the great floodlights that illuminated the Kremlin. It was a beautiful, tranquil moment. I stopped, looked towards the Kremlin roofs and drank in the serenity. I did not expect to be back and I was sad to be leaving.

When we reached our minibus, all tranquillity fled. Our driver was anxious to get us to the airport. His sense of urgency was made plain when we arrived. We joined everyone else in the great Soviet pastime of queuing. Moscow Airport presented particular frustrations to the traveller: when you arrive, you have to wait until they decide which side of the airport your flight's going to leave from. This happens about two hours before departure, but until it's announced you can do nothing. You then join the queue for the customs and wait while they check everybody, a reminder that this was after all the Soviet Union. Most countries are more concerned about who and what might be entering; the Soviets were more interested in departures. For this reason, they tended to be less exhaustive with foreigners, but only just. An hour's wait at customs was about average. After this you queue all over again at the ticket desk. We had time to dash into the duty-free shop, but discovered it was full of expensive foreign goods: we felt they were missing a trick here, as we would loved to have been able to buy some uniquely Russian things to take home.

Our Aeroflot seats had not been reservable, so the moment the flight was called was the signal for the start of a free-for-all to get on the plane. It's experiences like these that help you understand the culture, the mentality behind the way people behave and react to different situations. If you don't push and shove in Russia, you simply don't get on. Once we realized what was happening, we had to join in with the rest. Gordon and I ended up together in the two seats right at the back and chatted all the way back to London.

We were slightly concerned about having to appear on TV. We also wanted to know which of us would be chosen to begin training. In the morning we were taken to the Science Museum to meet the people there and to have a look around. As we went in, we found four huge portraits of us hanging from the roof; it's a disconcerting experience to glance up casually and find your own face beaming down at you. Our worries about dressing for TV were briefly allayed when they said clothes would be provided; a whole new realm of consternation opened up when we saw what they had prepared for us. The mission people fondly called the creations 'flying suits', but we promptly

dubbed them our Andy Pandy suits. As well as being irredeem-
ably naff, these one-piece jumpsuits that looked like cast-offs
from a Z-grade science fiction movie simply didn't fit. They all
had to be held in place with safety pins; the crotch of mine
dangled sexily somewhere between my knees.

To make us feel properly at home, a press conference was our
next distraction. We were suddenly nervous. Everyone from the
mission management was there, as well as a huge number of
journalists. Our discomfort with the Andy Pandy suits was
heightened when we discovered we were supposed to walk
through the assembled press to reach the platform.

We were relieved to change into our own slightly crumpled
clothes and flee back to the hotel for lunch.

My family arrived soon after we had returned to the museum
and changed back into the Andy Pandy suits. After only a few
minutes they were rushed away, but we had had long enough
together to establish that they hadn't been unduly messed
around with, or not at least any more than they had wisely
expected to be.

Even at this late stage, with quite a few years between now
and then and with all passion and expectation spent, I would
rather draw a veil over the excruciating experience of the
television show. It could be summed up as a Monty Python
sketch about four boffins who had accidentally entered Miss
World . . . but it wasn't as much fun as that might have been!
After a razzmatazz introduction, the four of us went to sit at
tables near the front of the audience. Some background material
about the mission and our selection process followed, but finally
the show went live to Moscow, where Jack Leeming, one of the
Antequera directors, announced my name and Tim's as the
successful candidates who would be going to Star City, while
Gordon and Clive would remain in Britain as our back-ups. Tim
and I returned to the stage, to huge applause. After a moment
Clive and Gordon came up and joined us, and then the four of us
just stood there, smiling and waving, smiling and waving. Tim

whispered to me urgently, 'Shake my hand and smile!', so I did so. The TV people were urging the audience to go on clapping; obviously the live show was under-running. I shook hands with Clive, and we both smiled, while Tim and Gordon did the same. What felt like an eternity of smiling went slowly by, live, in front of $5\frac{1}{2}$ million viewers.

At last it was over and I went back to my family's table. A few moments later, Tim and I were zoomed away downstairs for . . . yes, another press conference! More questions about how we felt. More photographs of us in our baggy Andy Pandy suits. Interviews followed, singly and together, and went on for what seemed like ages.

Finally we were rushed upstairs to a frantic champagne reception. All our families were there. I glimpsed Gordon and Clive on the other side of the room, managed a few words with them. Everyone wanted to talk to me and Tim. I held a glass of champagne untouched, until I got fed up of finding somewhere to put it when people asked me for my autograph. Very strange, signing autographs. Faces blurred past me: I saw one of the doctors who had looked after us in Moscow, one of the managers of Glavkosmos, the managing director from Mars Confectionery . . . but we were rushed past them all with hardly a chance to say hello.

Way back, at the meeting in Brunel University, in what now seemed like the mists of yesteryear, the Antequera people had warned us that they would 'own the butt' of the successful candidate. It had seemed, then, an aggressive, manneristic warning, a bit of hyped-up extremism thrown out to sound good to a large number of eager candidates, and not a warning that you could ever take seriously. Not in the real world. Now though, at last, I really felt owned, and yet in a circumstantial kind of way it was all by my own choice. I could have said no, refused the job, walked away. Yet I allowed or willed it to happen and I ended up, as warned, with my butt effectively owned. It was not at all a pleasant feeling.

By about 7 p.m. my family were fed up with waiting for me
and went back to their hotel. I promised I'd be along there as
soon as I could. I kept trying to break away, but every time I
turned someone else would want to talk to me, another
photographer would want some more pictures. At 8 p.m., Tim
and I managed to tear ourselves away. We grabbed a corner
upstairs, just to have a quiet chat with Gordon and Clive. We
separated after that; Tim went to a private party being thrown
by some of his friends and I slipped away back to my room at the
Grosvenor Hotel. I was still in the loathsome flying suit. I
grabbed some of my own clothes, then dashed over to my
family's hotel without changing. I found Andy's room and
changed into my own clothes. I was starting to slow down at
last, glimpse my former self. I was so glad to be there with them
all again, and with no one from television, or a PR company, or
from Antequera around us.

We all went downstairs for dinner. Andy told me she was due
to start a new job the following week. Life for her was changing,
too. It was a salutary moment. Over the last few weeks I had
thought of no one but myself and I realized how selfish this
selection process had made me become. Normal concerns swept
over me; I glimpsed the real world again.

The latter part of that evening turned out to be just a temporary
reprieve. At 9 a.m. the next day ITN phoned up to my room.
They wanted to film me going through the newspapers and I
duly obliged. Then a photographer from *The Times* turned up,
and took me and my family out into Hyde Park where, it
seemed, ducks needed to be fed. My family and I were tied up
doing this most of the morning; it was time spent together, but
without any opportunity to talk to each other. (In the end it
turned out they needn't have been there at all; when the
photograph appeared the next day it was, naturally, of me by
myself.)

The family did all have lunch together, but then a car picked me up. We collected Tim, then went on to a meeting with Peter Graham. This was not a happy meeting to begin with, but after a long talk, what diplomats call a frank exchange of views, the air began to clear. At the end of it all I felt unmistakably better. Why couldn't Antequera always treat us like this? Why the silences, the deliberate gaps in communication, the imposed periods hidden away from the world with no access to information?

By the end of the afternoon I longed to be by myself, at home, away from all this. Finally, I made it and in the middle of the evening I went back at last to my flat in Surbiton. The place was dark and cold; a huge pile of mail scraped on the floor as I pushed open the front door.

The telephone was ringing . . .

I was on the telephone for the rest of the evening, the remains of my old life scattered on the floor around me. I talked and talked, sometimes (at length) to friends who were calling to congratulate me or offer support, sometimes (more briefly) to reporters, but I was not able to stop. As soon as I put down the handset it would immediately start ringing again. Nowadays I would simply unplug the instrument or switch in the answering machine, but I didn't want to miss the voices of my friends.

Eventually, some time after midnight, I fell asleep. I keeled over on the carpet by the phone and that was where I still was when I woke up the next morning.

7

Looking Back on Earth

There is one matter that unites all astronauts, be they from the Soviet Union, the United States . . . or from anywhere else, including (and especially) Britain. They all love to stare out of the window.

They, we, never tire of it. I had a mere eight days first to discover then to succumb to the obsession, but Musa and Viktor, who had been in Mir for six months before we arrived, said that their preoccupation with looking through the windows remained as active as it had been from the start. Sergei, making his second visit to Mir, was just as fascinated by the view as the rest of us.

Mir orbits Earth at an average height of about 400 kilometres,[*] or roughly the distance from London to Holyhead. In absolute terms, then, it is not a great height, but such is the startling shallowness of our atmosphere that to all intents and purposes it is well into space.

The orbit Mir follows is at an angle of 51.6°, which means that the furthest it travels north is to the latitude of London,

---

[*] For practical purposes it is assumed that at such an altitude the station is in a vacuum. However, this is not entirely accurate and the orbit constantly decays. Every few weeks the cosmonauts (or mission control) have to boost the station back to its original height. At the end of May 1991 it was orbiting at about 364 kilometres above the Earth's surface.

and the furthest south it travels is to the Falkland Islands. It is not possible to see either of the polar ice-caps from the space station, but we *did* see ice. Much of Canada was white, as were some parts of the Soviet Union, and of course we passed over several mountain ranges, including the Alps and Himalayas, which were spectacularly snow-covered.

Each orbit takes ninety-two minutes, which means that the space station usually has sixteen periods of daylight (and darkness) in every twenty-four-hour period.

When the station passes over a daylit Earth, the window reveals the natural features of the world; at night, civilization manifests itself in the array of artificial lights with which we festoon our cities.

Our planet is endlessly, hypnotically beautiful.

It is also huge, which is something that rather took me by surprise. Like everyone else I had seen the photographs of Earth from space, especially those stunning ones taken during the Apollo missions, and I had also heard and read the words of earlier astronauts. The impression you get from them is one of Earth's smallness, its apparent fragility, its isolation in space.

It could simply be that the Apollo astronauts travelled further away from Earth than I did, so it just looked smaller, but my overriding impression was, and still is, of immensity. We were circling the Earth in about the same amount of time as it takes to watch the average feature film, and when I thought about it that way, yes, it did seem small. However, if you look down at what can be seen and try to establish a sense of where you are flying over at that time, and the scale of it, then it seems different.

For instance, we frequently crossed Western Europe and of course I could see the distinctive shape of Britain (often covered in cloud). I always had a warm and sentimental feeling whenever I could see parts of the world that I knew well or had visited. Down there were the people I knew and loved, my friends and family, and places that meant a lot to me.

In space, though, it would take us about five minutes to travel from Belfast to Hanover. Five minutes can drag by slowly when you're counting, but that is how long it took. By contrast, it took twenty minutes to cross Africa; when we crossed the Pacific it often took more than forty minutes before we were over landmass again. Suddenly I realized that the part of the world I knew, that before had seemed so enormous to me, could be traversed in about five of the ninety minutes. Thus the world acquired an immensity that until then had only been academic. It not only looked huge, it *felt* huge.

Twice every orbit we would cross the Equator, and whenever we did so in daylight I witnessed the extraordinary piling of clouds that occurs there. From space, looking towards the horizon, you can see the atmosphere. It looks like a thin blue shell hugging the surface: it seems barely deep enough to support life and this sight alone is a salutary reminder of how tenuous is our hold on this planet. As you approach the Equator, though, the height of the clouds below increases, rising up high into the atmosphere. Several times, as the space station moved north or south towards the Equator, and we looked tangentially ahead, it was as if there was a huge wall of cloud rising to meet us.

Clouds are, of course, a permanent feature of the view of Earth. The overall impression is of white clouds and blue sea: a white so bright when the sun reflects back that it hurts the eyes to look for too long, and a blue of an intensity that I had never experienced before. The land surface is physically easier to look at, in that the colours are more subtle, but it was not at all how I had imagined it would be.

In general, man-made features are difficult to see, unless they are in straight lines. Cities are indistinct, because they lack clear edges. While I was still in the Soyuz, moving up towards docking with Mir, I saw the south-eastern part of England. It seemed to consist of brown soil with bubbly greyer bits, which must have been the towns. Very uninspiring! I watched for London and Paris, two cities I thought I knew well, and saw only grey, undefined patches blending imperceptibly with the land around them. Both cities, I had thought, would be recognizable because of the distinctive rivers that flow through them, yet I could see neither. The Thames was briefly visible, but only in its upper reaches, where it straightens out slightly towards Oxford.

Straightness and lines are the main identifiers from space. Coasts and islands are of course easily distinguishable, if not instantly recognizable. On one occasion I saw a huge island, whose shape meant nothing to me; Sergei then recognized a particular river formation he had identified on his previous flight, and said the island was Madagascar. Forest fires can be seen easily, because the smoke from them streams out in a long straight line. Once, passing over the Australian outback, I saw two roads, each of them hundreds of miles long and running across the desert straight as a die, then meeting at a crossroads.

Overall, the impression you get of the Earth's land-surface is that much of it remains unused. Vast areas are the reddish-brown of desert; even those countries you know to be heavily populated appear to have large areas that have not been developed. Agriculture tends to look a dark grey, or a dull sage-green, whereas bare earth is fawn or brown, or a brick-red colour. When I was in space only two places looked green: Ireland, and the South Island of New Zealand. Sometimes, where there is a major irrigating river, such as the Nile where it passes through Egypt, you can easily see the river and how the agriculture around depends on it. The space perspective makes you realize just how much we depend on water and how there are vast areas of the world without it. In these places there are few signs of people or agriculture.

There are immense areas of the world that no one knows about, no one relates to. We sometimes think of the whole planet as our world, but the reality is that we are thinking only of the bit we know.

I have heard it said that national borders cannot be seen from space, but this is not strictly true. Some parts of the border between Canada and the USA are clearly marked, for instance, because of the different agricultural methods each country uses and because the border runs in a straight line. France looks different from the other European countries, because of the way their fields are laid out.

Human artefacts are, of course, most of what you can see on the night side of Earth. The continents gleam with yellow-white artificial lights, betraying the presence of civilization. These lights produce an enigma of their own, because although what you are seeing is not one huge source of light (the lights of, say, one city do not fuse into one blob), nor is it made up of strings of individual lights. Even so, you feel as if you can see individual lights, because of the way they form groups, even strings.

When you turn the other way and look into space, because you are away from the absorbing, dimming effect of the atmosphere, the immensity of space dazzles you. The stars out there are so thickly clustered, so bright and so many, you really feel as though you would have to push them aside to force a way through. Millions and millions of them! Then you look back at the Earth, and you realize that the light from those cities is going out to the stars, theoretically visible for ever, no matter how much it is diffused or dimmed on the way.

Electric storms at night were superb to witness from space. One lightning discharge would illuminate a whole radius of light around it and then set off another flash, which in turn would set off another somewhere else, like a chain reaction. It would traverse two hundred miles, quite easily, spreading rapidly, branching out, flaring and subsiding. Then another would flash somewhere else, setting off a new chain reaction. All this would take place over hundreds of miles! The people on Earth would have no idea of the true scale of the storm, because their experience of it would be local.

We saw a local event (one with global consequences) on the first night aboard the Soyuz capsule. I noticed a number of large, orange-red areas of light, and asked Sergei what he thought they might be. He stared a while, then said he had never seen them before. When we were on Mir we saw them again, but this time we located them to the north-western end of the Persian Gulf: they were the fires in the Kuwaiti oil-fields, after the Gulf War.

My realization that our concept of 'the world' is really the area we know best was true also of the space station. It was not long after we arrived that it began to feel like home. This was not just me; Sergei and Tolya remarked on it too. When I looked down at the Earth, I would think, 'That's my planet but it's no longer my *world.*' My world had become the space station. What became important to me was the safety of the station and the people inside it, and how we were living together.

When you look down from space you can't see individuals, or their relationships, the worries, hassles, involvements, delights, terrors. You simply see the area of land where they exist. In the same way you can observe the general location of a city, or you can see its lights at night, but you can't pick out individual streets or buildings, monuments or parks, and you can't sense its hustle and bustle. In short, you lose detail and see only the larger picture, and this has a calming effect. Details become less important.

Even so, for all the great times we were having in the space station, I knew that the planet below was home and that at some stage I would want to come back. I told the others about this and about the warm feelings that came over me whenever I saw Britain and Europe. They told me it happened to them too as they passed over the Soviet Union.

For the time being, though, the space station was my home and my feelings about it were more complete than I have ever felt for any flat or house I've lived in. After a while I could feel its every rotation. I felt the vibrations set up by the solar panels when they realigned themselves and I could hear the difference in the tone of the ventilators as the voltage fluctuated. This was not just a collection of modules and electronics: the station had life! To say I was sad to leave is an understatement to a major degree. If Mir ever re-enters the atmosphere and burns up, I know I will feel gutted, empty, as if losing a part of myself.

8

Preparing for Russia

I woke up on the floor of my flat in Surbiton, with the phone beside me. It was 7.30 a.m. and already too late for me to get to work at Mars on time.

What was I thinking! I was still technically employed by Mars, but I was under contract to Antequera and due to return to Moscow in three days' time. I picked up the phone to say I would try to get in to Mars later. My boss said at once: everything is under control, it's going to be fine, I'm sorting everything out. He mentioned my pension; it was being looked after. The P45; they would have it ready for me later. All this was a great relief, because it suddenly freed me to take care of a host of other pressing details. In the next three days I had to tidy away my old life, and frankly I found the prospect daunting.

In the afternoon I went up to London and by arrangement met Tim. Together we went to see Brian Harris, the lawyer. We made wills, and I signed over power of attorney to my father. It was a long afternoon of attending to detail, trying to anticipate all the things that might occur in the next few years. I got home at 8 p.m. I still had not had time to unpack from the trip to Moscow.

The next morning I went up to London again, this time to buy a long winter coat. I wanted to be able to look smart while staying warm. The immediate need was something to wear the next day, when I was due to meet the prime minister. My life for the last two or three years had made me habitually casual: I often used to ride to work on my motorbike, changing from my bike gear to factory whites, neither of which seemed suitable for the occasion.

I had time to get back to the flat, dump my new possessions, then I drove my car to work. This was the first time I had seen or driven the car since Kevin had collected it for me after it had been serviced. I saw my manager, emptied my locker and picked up some of the paperwork. What I really would have liked to do was get across to the other end of the huge factory where my friends still worked, but I simply didn't have the time.

I drove back through the early rush hour. As I went along the corridor to my flat, I saw someone waiting outside my door. At first glance, in the dimly lit passage, I thought it was a schoolboy waiting for a friend outside the wrong flat.

'Miss Sharman?' said the young man, as I approached. 'I'm from the *Mirror*. I wonder if you would answer a few questions?'

At that particular moment it was, quite literally, the last thing I wanted to do. I tried to side-step him, but he moved deftly to block my way.

'I'm sorry,' I said. 'I simply don't have time for an interview.'

I was trying to find my key, wondering what I would do if he attempted to force his way into the flat with me. I couldn't stop him being in the hallway, but surely it would be trespass if he tried to follow me in? I got the door open, gave him what I hoped would look like a farewell smile and pushed determinedly through with all my stuff. Even then his leg was outstretched and I had to step over him. Fortunately, he knew the limits of his access to me and didn't try to follow me in.

I could hear him outside for some time afterwards, but I closed my mind to him and got down to sorting out some of the hundreds of loose ends in my life. It was a truly unpleasant

Mars Confectionery is proud to announce another vacancy.

Until recently, Helen Sharman was working as a research technologist for Mars Confectionery. Now she's in Moscow, training for the Anglo-Soviet space mission, JUNO.

As a company dedicated to helping individuals attain their full potential, we are proud to be associated with her achievement. Now we want more people like her.

Our continuing commitment to excellence depends on appointing high-calibre women and men into *every* discipline. We are currently looking for more stars in research and technology, as well as in manufacturing and finance.

If you enjoy working with the best, and are keen to explore your career potential to the full – whatever your present role – find out more about life at Mars.

As an equal-opportunity employer, we welcome applications from women and men. Call Dorreen Campbell on 0753 514627, or send her your detailed cv at Mars Confectionery, Dundee Road, Slough, Berkshire SL1 4JX.

Mars

credit: *Media System*

The job ad Mars Confectionery used later to find my replacement.
Here, the *better* half of the Andy Pandy suit can be seen.

feeling, to know that I could not leave my flat without having to run the gauntlet of a reporter. (Fortunately, he must have grown bored with waiting for me to reappear, because when I next went out he had gone. I did not see him again.)

My last full day in England was dominated by my meeting with Margaret Thatcher.

One of the Granard Rowland people happened to live fairly close to me and he called round early to pick me up. The plan was that everyone (Tim Mace, of course, and some of the Antequera management) would meet up in the vicinity of Downing Street. What no one had anticipated was that it would be a foggy day and that there was an awful lot of traffic. We only just got there in time. Most of the others were already there, waiting in a car in Whitehall, but of Tim there was no sign. His driver had phoned in to say they were stuck in fog and traffic on the M3.

Someone suggested I would have to go in to see Mrs Thatcher on my own. My immediate reaction was that that would be unfair; the whole point of everything we had gone through to that stage was that Tim and I were together in this. It seemed impossible to me that I could go in there on my own. Then I had second thoughts. It was the only opportunity I would have to represent Tim and myself before we went off to Russia; surely it would be better to represent him than for neither of us to be there at all?

By this time we had walked the short distance along Downing Street and had been ushered into a waiting room on the ground floor. It was fortunate for all concerned that the prime minister was already in another meeting which was running late. While we were waiting, and to everyone's relief, Tim suddenly arrived. He just had time to whip off his scarf when we were told that the prime minister would see us. We all walked upstairs. I was intensely glad to see Tim.

We were to meet Mrs Thatcher in one of the function rooms on the first floor, and here, already assembled, were the usual battery of photographers. Mrs Thatcher entered the room, shook hands with us both, then instantly took control of the situation.

She stepped forward and addressed the photographers directly.

'Now then,' she said to them. 'I think we have, yes, one minute.' She looked deliberately at her wristwatch. 'I think this would make a rather nice photograph, underneath the archway here, just by the door. How about if I stand in the middle, Helen here, and how about Tim on the other side? Is this all right for you?'

So we stood there in a little group and they clicked away. Mrs Thatcher chatted to me and then she turned to Tim and chatted to him. The photographers were completely free to take whatever pictures they liked. At the end of the minute, though, Mrs Thatcher said, 'Thank you *very* much!' and turned towards the doorway behind us. We then followed her into the room and closed the doors. That was it. The press had vanished.

In these sixty seconds with Mrs Thatcher I learned more about staying in control of such chaotic photo 'opportunities' than I had been able to in all the previous five months. She put Tim and myself at ease, she gave the photographers their chance to get the pictures and yet she stayed in control, starting and ending the session efficiently and courteously. It was a real insight into how to deal with these situations and it was deeply ironic to me to remember how Antequera's PR people (whom we had been told were experienced media professionals) had told us again and again that we must do exactly what the press wanted, that we had to defer to their wishes, no matter what. In my experience, that led to nothing but hassles.

When we were alone with Mrs Thatcher she was not in a rush and appeared to have a great deal of time for us. While we chatted over coffee she seemed unhurried and able to give us all her attention. In addition, she was well briefed or well informed, even though the Soviet space program was clearly not her subject. She knew how to obtain information without appearing ignorant. It was again a disarming experience. I was by this time so used to being interviewed by journalists who, broadly ignorant of the subject and unwilling or unable to brief themselves adequately, would presume the same level of ignorance in their readership . . . and as a result obtain an interview worthless to all.

After what seemed like an extravagant amount of the prime minister's time, she brought the interview gracefully to an end. She said, 'Well, thank you so much for coming along,' and it was obvious the time had come to make ourselves scarce. Her manner remained unhurried, though; she chatted to us as we walked to the door, then shook our hands again as we made our departure.

A number of reporters were waiting for us in Downing Street itself and we could not avoid giving a brief impromptu press conference. A fresh difficulty presented itself: we had been instructed to shun BBC News, because ITV was a potential sponsor. This was an awkward instruction to carry out, especially as we were constantly being thrown unprotected into these problems. The PR company had not exactly stepped forward to help us out. Both Tim and I found this tricky and embarrassing. With hindsight (partly gained through having witnessed Mrs Thatcher's skilful media handling) it seems a crude and amateurish way of trying to manipulate the media.

From Downing Street we were rushed away for a photo call with Memorex, another sponsoring company. On the way I gave the mission director the keys to my car, because by arrangement Antequera was buying my car from me. 'Here are the keys,' I said. 'The car is parked in the yard at the back of my flat.' That was it, that had to be it. No time for the finer details.

Soon afterwards we arrived for the photo session with Memorex and dutifully, awkwardly, posed for the cameras.

At 1 p.m. I headed back to Surbiton in the car Granard Rowland had provided. When we were halfway there the phone rang. I was staring sleepily at the houses slipping by and barely noticed. Then the driver uttered those words that are always a surprise away from home, 'It's for you.' It was Granard Rowland, who at this last minute had come up with an exciting chance to do an interview! Could I go up to Leicester to do an interview? 'No, no,' I said. 'I have other things to do. I'm flying to Russia in the morning.' I put the phone down, realized that some finer spirit had had the confidence to emerge and feeling fairly proud of myself I promptly feel asleep.

Almost as soon as I was back at home I had to go out again, this time locally, to the bank, the building society, the post office, getting my address changed and generally sorting out more of the details. I rushed home afterwards to pack. I read through and sorted out all the legal documents. I paid a few bills. I made up a huge envelope of stuff to send up to Dad. I wrote to the lawyers. The phone rang several times.

I had finished as far as I was able to by 2 a.m. I hadn't eaten for hours and I was exhausted. I staggered to the fridge and there I found a Marathon bar and a quarter-bottle of Moët & Chandon. The former was a leftover from my days at Mars; the latter was identified by a note as being from my good friend Les, a neighbour who had the only other key to my apartment.

I wolfed down the chocolate bar, then consumed the champagne at a more leisurely rate. That was my dinner that evening. Thanks, Les.

The doorbell went at 6.50 a.m. the next day, but I was already up and about, trying to finish off the last-minute stuff. Thinking it was Scottish TV (they had arrived five minutes earlier, their documentary unfinished; I had made them wait outside in the hall), I pulled the door open grudgingly. It was Clive Smith.

'Hello,' he said. 'I thought you'd like a hand with getting your stuff to the airport.'

I fell on him with glad cries of happiness. A friend indeed. He waited while I checked around the flat one more time, then helped me down with all the luggage.

The car arrived on time at 7 a.m. For some reason I was gratified to discover that it was huge! Clive and I and all my stuff fitted into it with abundant space to spare. We were ahead of most of the rush hour, and so we were at Heathrow with lots of time to spare. Clive and I went to one of the cafés for a long chat. At 8.30 a.m. I checked in and soon afterwards located Cathy Judelson, the interpreter who was flying to Moscow with us. STV conscientiously filmed as many of these exciting and unusual events as they could.

I had remembered to bring the documents for my car and I handed them over to the manager from Antequera, who had also just arrived.* The members of the press were gathering and, feeling conspicuous in the middle of Heathrow with hundreds of other travellers, I agreed to one more photo call. Now we were so close to the end, the very end, I found this last session more tedious than ever. Finally, armed with my Memorex walkman, I went through into the departure lounge with Cathy. STV soon followed. They were there as we all boarded the plane, filming our last moments in Britain. It seemed an apt farewell.

Three hours later we landed in Moscow. Tim's plane arrived an hour after ours.

---

* The following summer, in the middle of May, my father received a letter from the police. It told him that my car had been found apparently abandoned in a car park somewhere in London, with thousands of pounds' worth of accumulated parking charges.

Right
Space
Station
Mir

Below The
module
and Earth

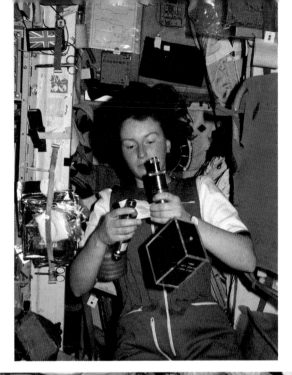

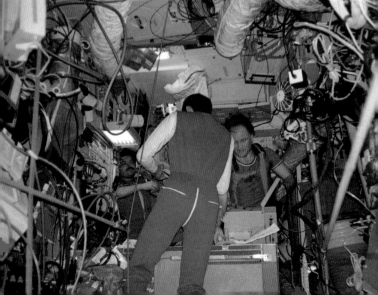

Opposite page, above
Helen with biological
experiments on Mir

Right Helen's bedroom.
The sleeping bag is
attached to the wall.
The black circle is the
window.

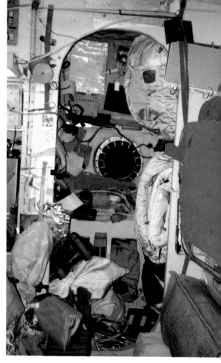

Left Musa, Sergei and
Viktor in the base block

Right Helen in her
sleeping bag

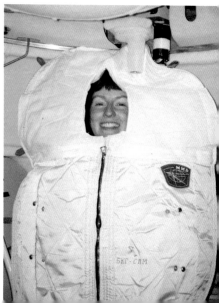

Salt Lake

THE VIEW FROM MIR

A crossroads in the Northern American States

Western England, Wales and Ireland from space

THE VIEW FROM MIR

Cape Cod

Dusk . . .

and sunrise

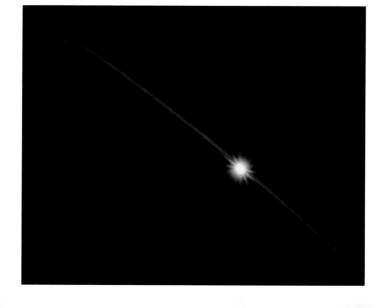

Above Musa, Sergei, Helen and Viktor calling
Mission Control for the last time before
leaving the station

Below The rescue team arrives

Above Home at last

Below Walking to the helicopter

9

12 EXPERIMENTS, 125,000 SEEDS AND SOME SNAILS

Work in Space

As far as scientists are concerned, a space station has two supreme advantages over anywhere on Earth: it is in a condition of 'weightlessness', and it is surrounded by a 'vacuum'. Experiments can be carried out in space that simply cannot be attempted on Earth.

I've always enjoyed finding out about things and trying to explain what is happening in a way that we poor humans can understand (I'm sure we're not the most intelligent species in the universe) is a challenge that scientists constantly take up. Faced with a different set of conditions and the ability to look at processes in a new light was something I was looking forward to. Without the acceleration due to gravity, a complicating factor usually experienced on Earth, it might be possible to understand much more about some of the systems and concepts that interested me so much, and of course there was always the possibility of finding out something about which I knew absolutely nothing before. It was one of the reasons that I had applied to be an astronaut in the first place.

However, even space is not an entirely perfect or unblemished place. Since weight is the product of gravity on mass, pure weightlessness could only be achieved if *all* gravitational effects were nullified or balanced. As every body in the universe exerts a gravitational effect on all the others, the probability of finding a place anywhere in the universe where these gravitational fields will cancel each other out is small and to be so far away from any massy object that there is no acceleration due to gravity is at the moment only possible in theory. Certainly, a spot 364 kilometres above the surface of the Earth is not it. Scientifically, then, pure weightlessness cannot be achieved.

In the same way, a perfect vacuum would be defined as a region that contains no matter. Since space itself is mostly devoid of matter it is practical to think of it as a vacuum, and treat it as such, but in reality outer space is littered with physical matter, from meteors and hunks of spacecraft to subatomic particles. The density of this material does vary, but for many purposes it cannot be ignored.

Experimental data obtained on the space station therefore have to take these factors into account, as well as the local effects of small accelerations caused by the station itself and its orbit. This arises in several different ways. Most of it is caused by vibration and rotation of the station, but the Earth is not a pure, homogeneous sphere and the orbit of the space station isn't entirely circular, but slightly elliptical (causing the station to accelerate and decelerate as it orbits the planet). To some extent these effects can be minimized by the experimenter. While carrying out certain experiments you make sure, for instance, that no one is exercising on the treadmill, or that the space station is not about to be moved. With these kinds of precaution, and an understanding of the limitations on the condition, the station is an ideal laboratory for certain kinds of experiments.

It was my job, as a scientifically qualified cosmonaut, to oversee a number of experiments during my short stay on Mir. I carried out a range of them while I was there, from medical tests to physical and chemical research.

I conducted the medical tests on myself, starting with the

wearing of electrodes on my heart for a continuous twenty-four-hour period. This measured the way my heart was beating in comparison with pre-flight and post-flight recordings.

Also of interest to medical researchers is the way mental coordination and reaction speed might vary before, during and after spaceflight. An experiment called 'Prognos' allowed me to monitor this through measured reactions to a series of randomized lights. These appeared in different patterns and combinations. I would memorize the pattern; when future patterns appeared I would have to remember the first and how it differed from what had just appeared, or be able to spot it when it appeared again. The instrument recorded whether I was right and how long I took.

I also took samples of my own blood by pricking the end of my finger. I had to take about twelve samples a day, so you can imagine that by the time I returned to Earth my fingers bore an uncanny resemblance to pin-cushions!

An incidental point of these medical experiments was the fact that I was only in space for a total of eight days. Most of the Soviet cosmonauts go up for extended periods, usually several months, so they now have many test results on long-stay subjects, but not on the shorter-term people. My work was intended to help fill this gap.

One of the minor problems associated with spacecraft is that in 'weightless' conditions dust does not settle. Because of the constant human activity on board Mir, the movement of so many objects around the station, so much food being consumed, hair and whiskers being snipped off, epidermal flaking and so on, the air becomes pretty dusty. Cosmonauts tend to sneeze a lot: I found myself sneezing on average about twenty to thirty times an hour.[*] The researchers were interested in the amount of dust found throughout the station and what was in it. I took

---

[*] On Mir the air is constantly moved, filtered and cooled by the ventilating fans, but much dust remains. A similar situation exists on the American Shuttles.

samples of air at various points in the station, collected the filter papers and brought them back.

As part of the biological experiments I grew some wheat seedlings, researching into the possibility one day of growing food in space. By the time I was able to set up this experiment the seedlings had been 'weightless' and in the dark for two days, so their roots and shoots were all over the place. I put them by a light, and when I went back four hours later to water them, all the shoots were growing towards the light, while the roots remained chaotic. For similar reasons I took some potato roots up to the station, trying to learn about early growth phases in these. (I have since found out that potatoes have been grown from the tissue culture I brought back.)

Another aspect of being in space is that although you may remain within the Earth's normal magnetic field, the altitude does introduce experimentally significant differences. I had other seeds that I grew in a non-uniform magnetic field, placing magnets around them at certain positions. I first had to start the seeds growing in water, then I halted the growth in a fixating medium, so I knew exactly how long they had been growing and what the orientation of the magnetic field had been.

Although I did no actual work with them, I took some snails up with me, kept them in a part of the station that was subject to a minimum of vibrations, then brought them back.

We took up a tiny lemon tree, so small as almost to be a bonsai. The idea of this was to see if higher plants can actually be kept alive in space. This will be important in the future if we want to be self-sufficient in space, such as during a long journey to Mars or one of the other planets. We know we can grow seeds, but producing fruit or flowers inside a spacecraft is still a largely unknown quantity.

An experiment called 'Vita' was one in which it was possible to mix the contents of different cells with different media, trying to dissolve the cell walls, mix the contents, then grow the cells and make them replicate.

I took up 125,000 seeds for later distribution to British schoolchildren, sponsored by the seed company Suttons. All I had to do was look after two separate samples: one which went with me into space, the other, the control sample, which went with me everywhere *but* into space. These seeds were later sorted out and distributed by Suttons, so that each school received some seeds from each sample. The children could then monitor the growth, noting what differences, if any, might appear.

Finally, there were two on-board experiments I found particularly interesting. The first was growing luciferase protein crystals. On Earth you can't grow the crystals big enough because convection currents arise in the solution as the crystals form. Using a number of different concentrations, temperatures, times and pressures, I was able to grow the same crystal, determining which conditions were best for its growth. When I brought them back the crystals were big enough to be analysed by X-ray crystallography, so it would have been possible to determine the structure of the protein. From this the design of medicines can be based. These crystals cannot be produced large enough on Earth.

My favourite experiment of all was the electrotopographical experiment. We had taken up with us a number of different thin films of ceramic oxides which were to be exposed to the 'vacuum' outside. One of the things we were looking at was possible future coatings for the outside of spacecraft, and how they would react to being exposed to space. Ceramics are being increasingly used in space; for instance, the tiles used on the NASA Shuttle are ceramic. Another application in the future would be in high-temperature superconductors.

I liked the electrotopographical experiment because it meant using a particular chamber on the space station which could be opened up to the outside. When I had mounted the ceramic films I would put them into the chamber, close it off, evacuate it, then open it up to the other side. After a few hours I would bring the films back in. This is the only other time I remember that smell of raw metal, which I noticed when the hatch of the Soyuz was first opened. One other feature of this experiment was that the chamber we used was located in a terribly awkward part of the space station, right underneath the table! Of course, in 'weightless' conditions any particular location should not be any more awkward than any other, but it took at least two of us to operate this chamber. Three made it even easier. We would all gather around and anyone coming into that part of the space station would see us with our heads inside the chamber, backs and legs hanging out at all angles.

I had one other job to do, but it blended so closely with my passion for staring out of the window that I barely thought of it as work. I had to make some visual observations of the Earth and to carry out these I used an instrument enabling me to assess different colours accurately. I had to look specifically for the appearance of different colours on the surface of the Earth and use a colorimeter to make a match. The measurements I made could be reproduced back on Earth, so that the scientists would know exactly what colour that part of the surface looked like from space. From that they could work out, for instance, the concentration of salt in that particular area, or what type of forestry might be growing there, or how much water.

10

Training

I arrived in Star City to start cosmonaut training on 30 November 1989 and was based there until after the mission, eighteen months later. It was probably the most significant period of my life, in its own way even more influential on my outlook and ideas than the time I spent in space.

Quite apart from the theoretical and practical training for the mission, in itself a considerable challenge, I had a lot to contend with. I was suddenly immersed in a society about which I had known almost nothing in advance, in a country where I did not speak the language, with hardly anyone around me who knew my own country or language and for much of the time with my own status as a trainee astronaut formally and financially uncertain. Earlier in life I had felt a sense of disappointment when learning curves started to level off; in the Soviet Union I was confronted by one which seemed to rise towards infinity.

Learning the Russian language was the priority. Apart from listening to the tapes in my car a few times, and the two weeks in Hospital No. 6, I knew nothing about it. Learning Russian presents special problems to anglophones, of which getting to grips with the Cyrillic alphabet is the first but by no means the greatest.

An extra dimension to the difficulties, which I did not fully appreciate until I was actually in Russia, is that the way English-speaking travellers can usually get by was not possible. In other countries a handful of phrases will often suffice, helped out with sign-language and pointing, and by the discovery that most shopkeepers, hoteliers and so on do understand a smattering of English. This was not so in Star City. English-speaking visitors were comparatively rare and most ordinary people have never had a reason to learn the language. If anything, they tended to have a few words of German, a relic of the Soviet Union's relationship with East Germany.

As for sign-language, while it might be relatively easy to wander into a shop in Italy, say, and point expressively at the kind of cheese or fruit you would like to buy, the same situation rarely arose in Moscow. After queuing for an hour or two in a blizzard, you were likely to be confronted by empty showcases, empty shelves and an assistant who spoke no English and who was waiting for you to ask for what you wanted.

Anyway, my needs of the language were more intense than those of a tourist or shopper. We were going to be taught scientific and technical subjects in Russian; later we would need to have a grasp of the language good enough for us to communicate safely with other cosmonauts without groping for a dictionary, and perhaps even have to deal with life-or-death situations.

I had my first Russian lesson five days after I arrived, although of course in the days before this I had been trying to converse with all the people I had been meeting. The first lesson was terribly confusing: the teacher talked (in Russian) about linguistic features such as second pretonics, and concentrated on pronunciation. By lunchtime I was on the point of giving up, but Cathy Judelson, who was with us for the first few days, made it much easier by explaining it in simple English terms. Unexpectedly, the next day things started to become slightly familiar and I found the language easier. That evening I wanted to book a telephone call to my parents (discovering, incidentally, that because I was in Star City I was in a privileged position, as I only had to order the call one hour in advance; most Russians had to book two or three days ahead) and had to arrange it with the operator in Russian.

By the standards ordinary Soviet citizens were used to I was given fairly spacious accommodation in Star City. I had a flat to myself, with a living room, two bedrooms, a kitchen and a bathroom. It was sufficiently well furnished and equipped that I could cater for myself if I wished, even though much of the equipment seemed pretty dated and inefficient by Western standards. It had everything I needed and more (in fact it was much bigger than the flat in London I had just left!), though I missed being able to make fresh coffee, or to cook a quick meal in a microwave oven. There was a colour TV in the living-room (although the picture was always in various shades of green), but there was no way of playing music. I was not destined to spend much time alone in this apartment, simply because everyone I met was so friendly and welcoming, but at first it seemed very strange, and I felt a long way from home.

Tim and I weren't the only language students in Star City. A few days after our lessons began I was having tea in the canteen, when I was joined by a cosmonaut from Ukraine. He had just had two lessons in English and asked if he could practise it with me. This was my first meeting with Tolya!

The Russian lessons continued for another three months, the dry concentration on linguistic technicalities balanced out by regular sessions of sport or physical training. Star City was equipped with superb sporting facilities and Tim and I had full access to them. We ran and swam, went cross-country skiing in the winter and lifted weights in the gym (the exercise I most disliked). We spun ourselves sideways in a wheel, increasing then decreasing the speed, then stopping and accelerating in the opposite direction. This was to confuse the balance mechanism in the ear and accustom us to another aspect of weightlessness –

though we thought it was just another attempt to make us sick! My favourite activity was on the trampoline, where we would tumble forwards, backwards, backwards again, then twist and so on, as our trainer shouted commands.

Oddly enough, it was through these sessions that we really learnt to speak Russian. No matter how much vocabulary you learn or how many irregular verbs you cram in, there is no substitute for living in a country, talking to its people, interacting on a daily basis with colleagues, friends, people you meet at parties and so on. When I look back on the early months in Star City, I know that I probably learnt most of my Russian in the saunas we all took after swimming.

Now that I have touched on the social side of life in Star City, I should say that life would probably have been intolerable if the Russians were not such a hugely generous race of people. I soon lost count of the small and large gestures of hospitality and friendship I received in the early days, and as the months went by I began to make some of the best friends in my life.

When I set out, though, I could count on none of this. Tim Mace and I left Britain without knowing anyone at all in the Soviet Union, beyond the few people we had briefly met during the medicals. Of course we had each other, but we had been thrown together by chance and circumstance and would certainly never have met if the Juno selection procedure had not put us together.

In the first few weeks and months, Tim and I stayed close and supported each other as and how we could. We naturally saw each other as islands of familiarity in the ocean of strangeness in which we found ourselves. We particularly felt this need when we had glimpses of what we had left behind; we were sometimes asked to receptions at the British Embassy, and the return afterwards to Star City would renew our feelings of alienation and isolation. Many such times would find us staying up together late into the night, talking in English, of ourselves and our own lives.

In the work our different backgrounds and personalities did not provide a clash, as I think we had both rather suspected they might; on the contrary we tended to complement each other. For instance, I had difficulty coming to terms with the military way of thinking and of doing things, because it made little sense to me. Tim, being used to it, would just accept it. When we were being taught some of the aeronautical theory, he had an advantage over me because he had already studied it and he would be a great help to me. However, when we moved on to subjects like the growing of crystals, it was the other way around.

We became, and remained, close friends, but inevitably our interests were different. As we became more familiar with the life, as we literally found out how to do things in that deeply bureaucratic and difficult society, our social lives began to diverge. Tim had little or no interest in the arts, for instance, yet to me the exhibitions, museums, theatres and concert halls of Moscow were irresistible. Eventually we both had our own groups of friends in Star City and Moscow and the heavy mutual dependence began to wane a little.

Physically moving around was fairly difficult by the standards I had grown used to in Britain. There was a public railway line that ran from Star City into Moscow which was reasonably convenient for commuting to the capital. The trouble was that our trainers in Star City discouraged us from using the railway. They warned of possible trouble, especially late at night. It was always easy to forget that what for me represented a kind of temporary freedom, seemed to them a needless endangering of an expensively trained cosmonaut. One night on the train, when I was returning late from the theatre, I had a narrow escape from a gang of drunken men and began to see the trainers' point.

I hungered for my own car. Ironically, in our relatively privileged position in Star City, we had the use of chauffeur-driven Volgas. They had to be paid for, of course, and booked up a day in advance, but it meant we would be driven swiftly and safely to and from our destinations. It maybe sounds ungracious to say it, but I often preferred to use the public train. While I was being driven it meant I couldn't explore on my own, or make spontaneous decisions about places to go.

For much of 1990 the whole future of the mission was in doubt and Tim and I could have been sent back to England at a few days' notice, but by August I had had enough. There was a Finnish shop in Moscow which would import Ford motor cars, so when I was in London later that month I phoned Helsinki and ordered a Ford Escort (a completely basic model, but for one concession to the climate: it had heated seats). They put it on a train to Moscow for me and it was as simple as that!

Less easy was actually getting it on the road. It had to be stored in the embassy compound until it was issued with number plates. This brought me face to face with Soviet bureaucracy. In Moscow foreigners have to have number plates that designate them as foreigners. People working in embassies have plates which are designated by colour for the diplomatic or technical corps. If you work in an accredited business out there, the plate has an 'M'. There's also a 'P' plate for those cars to be exported. However, I fitted none of these definitions. I was British, but I was not with the embassy; I was working, but not for a company. On top of everything I was living in an area where foreigners were forbidden! In the end they gave me an 'H' plate, used by some other people in business, apparently some kind of bureaucratic compromise; but the car was stored in the embassy compound for more than a month before I could have it. Life improved immeasurably afterwards.

In fact, the material side of life had been improving since the beginning of that year. Although I had been given a big flat to myself in Star City (one that I knew was much larger than the average family flat in Moscow), the sheer inconvenience of daily life in the Soviet Union had been brought home to me several times in the first few weeks: for just one example, it sometimes took up to two weeks before clothes and bedding washed in the official laundry could be collected.

When we made a brief return to London for Christmas I spent a useful morning in the West End, buying a huge quantity of household items, including a microwave oven, a washing machine, a kettle, piles of stationery and dozens of books, and arranging for the whole lot, with my hi-fi system (sheer luxury), to be shipped to Star City. They arrived before the end of February and thereafter I was able to exist in a fair degree of personal comfort. Having my own tapes with me made me realize how important music was in my life.

Something was amiss with Antequera; Tim and I kept picking up signs we did not like. Most of our contact with the Antequera office in London was by telephone, which meant that for us it was a frustrating hit-or-miss affair whenever we tried to get through. (When you have had to book a call in advance and are greeted by an engaged signal, or no one answers, or you are told that the person you wished to speak to is out of the office or in a meeting . . . it is intensely disappointing, to say the least, and produces feelings of irritation out of all proportion.) However, contact was maintained and to a large extent we were kept abreast of what was going on.

They were always vague about the sponsorship deals, though, and without these the entire mission would almost certainly fall through. We knew a few companies had agreed to put up some money, but there was a huge shortfall. Whenever we asked directly, the answers we were given instantly went into a surreal spectrum that ranged from high enthusiasm at one end ('Everything's just *marvellous!*') to equivocation at the other ('We're just about to sign a deal with someone else'), but we weren't stupid. We knew we were not hearing the whole story.

During our brief trip back to the UK over Christmas nothing was settled either way, but in the middle of February Peter Graham rang from London to say he had resigned from Antequera. No reason was given. The following week Jack Leeming, one of the directors of Antequera, came over from England to see us and to break the bad news. The story was that not enough sponsorship money had been raised and this was basically because the mission could not be guaranteed. It was a classic chicken-and-egg situation: no mission unless there is enough money, no money unless the mission is definite.

The only good news was that we were to continue training for the time being. How this was to be paid for and how the mission itself would eventually be funded we were not told. With not much choice available, we carried on training as before.

This indefinite situation continued for most of 1990 and it was a distraction and a worry whenever we thought about it. Most of the time we did not, partly because we were in the middle of a hectic training schedule and partly because without any hard information to go on there was little point in dwelling on the problem.

Finally, in December of that year, word reached us that the mission was definitely on again: Moscow Narodny Bank had become our white knight. The bank had made an agreement with Energia and accepted full responsibility for the mission. Antequera had been dissolved. Again, in practical terms, this formal reorganization made no difference to Tim and me. We continued training, just as before, but now there was a distinct sense that an unspoken burden had been lifted from us.

The real sense of isolation that I have described may give the impression that we were virtual prisoners in Star City, but this is far from the case. Between the end of November 1989 and my flight eighteen months later I was able to get back to the West on six separate occasions, including both Christmas periods (even though Christmas was not an official holiday in the Soviet Union), and a month's holiday in the summer of 1990. In addition, friends of mine came out from England and stayed with me for a couple of weeks in the summer, followed soon after by my family.

Only the first trip back to Britain, for Christmas 1989, was a hectic reminder of the weeks leading up to selection, and that was because Antequera had set up a seemingly endless round of interviews and press conferences. Their lack of attention to detail also obliged me to spend the whole of a valuable day at the Soviet Embassy in London, trying to obtain new visas for Tim and myself. Even so, I was able to spend Christmas with my family and also find the time to buy all those luxurious necessities to see me through the rest of my stay.

On later trips I was either more circumspect with the news of my return to the UK, or else I simply gave the place a miss. One of my trips was a long weekend in Paris; in the summer break I went hiking in fabulous anonymity in the Swiss Alps; and I spent Christmas 1990 in the USA.

I am often asked if life in Russia made me miss Britain. At first, everything was of course a novelty and in the whirl of meeting so many people, struggling with the language and trying to settle down I didn't have much time to miss anything. Then, gradually, I began to notice how difficult some things were to do or obtain. I have already mentioned phonecalls; while I was in Russia there were only thirteen lines to the United Kingdom available for public use. Fresh fruit and vegetables were comparatively rare, although available at an inflated price in Moscow's markets. As is well known, you have to queue for just about everything. In expecting differences you overlook similarities. Just before Christmas in 1989 I happened to be in Moscow's Gorki Street, and was amazed at the crowds of shoppers. The following week I was in London's Oxford Street, and there seemed to me actually fewer people out and about than there had been in Moscow.

What I really did miss was people. Not only my family and friends, but also the more general sense of being in a country where there is a sub-text of cultural understanding, where you can relax with friends and make allusions and asides and silly jokes without having to explain laboriously as you go.

In the broadest terms, my training for the mission fell into three general areas.

In the first place there was suitability training, which began, in a sense, with the selection procedure in Britain. It included physical and medical fitness and a familiarity with written, spoken and technical Russian. In the later stages this also included a great deal of academic work, learning the technical and scientific theories behind space operations: the theory of flight, orbital dynamics, how the fuel system in the rocket works and so on. Secondly, there was practical training, in particular parachuting, weightlessness and emergency drills. Finally, there was crew training, in which I worked in the ground-based simulators with the other members of my crew, learnt my way around Soyuz and Mir, practised the launch and re-entry procedures and prepared the experimental work.

The first, and perhaps hardest hurdle was learning Russian, but by the beginning of March Tim and I were declared proficient enough in the language to be given academic training. We had in fact already started some of the practical training. In February we had begun learning how to use a parachute and in the last week of that month we went up in a helicopter with the two trainee Japanese cosmonauts to put the training into practice.

It was a beautiful winter's day, with thick snow on the ground and a surface air temperature of $-15°C$. I felt no apprehension at all until we were at the point where we were about to make the first jump. Ryoko* was the first to go, and as she stood at the open hatch of the helicopter, staring down at the ground, I did feel a strong wave of nervousness. Then she jumped, the static line cracked sharply behind her and we could see her floating down safely to the ground. By the time it was my turn, all nerves had gone.

Once I was falling away from the helicopter, what most struck me was the tranquillity of the descent. I could hear sounds from the ground, although they were muffled, and somewhere around me there were birds singing. My arrival on the ground went as planned, made perhaps a little softer than normal by the amount of snow.

The second descent was even more enjoyable and I was game for as many more as they would allow me. Unfortunately, I was now mission-assigned. My well-being and safety were no longer my exclusive concern. Two jumps were all I was to be allowed.

A month later we were initiated into the pleasures of weightlessness. This happens inside the specially modified cargo compartment of an Ilyushin 76 heavy freighter. The state of weightlessness is simulated by the aircraft flying a parabolic loop: the pilot makes it climb steeply, levels it off, then dives. The flight trajectory follows a parabola, so that in the dive the aircraft and its occupants are falling, or accelerating towards the ground, at the same rate. The effect is that for between 20 and 30 seconds the occupants become weightless. Although you are afforded merely a glimpse of what real weightlessness is like, these short periods do allow the trainers to take you through various preparatory sessions. This is a fairly dangerous procedure, with several hundred tonnes of jet aircraft performing steep dives and recoveries, and so we had to wear parachutes – hence the parachute training earlier on. We also had ECG

* Ryoko Kikuchi, who worked for the same Japanese television company as Toyohiro Akiyama. She was in the back-up crew for Toyohiro's mission.

electrodes attached, so that our physical reactions could be monitored.

The aircraft goes through ten parabolic loops on each flight. They made us sit still in the first, so we could find out what was going to happen and how it would feel. On the second loop we were allowed to try moving around a bit at a time. Then we moved from the floor to the ceiling of the cabin . . . in each case making sure we were back on the floor, and holding on, before the plane went into its recovery.

On later flights we learnt to move sideways across the cabin, from one wall to the other. Ryoko and I practised moving objects with a large mass, by passing a medicine ball to and fro. On another flight we were given a 50-kilo weight to move around, and then a large solar panel to open. Many of the objects that had to be moved around on the space station would be bulky and massy, and we had to know how to handle them. The point of all this is that although weight disappears, mass remains the same. An object we think of as 'heavy' on Earth is simply something with a lot of mass being acted upon by gravity; temporarily eliminate the effect of the gravity and the same object will float as any other . . . until you come to move it, when you discover it's not only hard to get it moving, it is equally difficult to make it stop.

Later we repeated all these exercises, this time wearing spacesuits. From here we learnt how to put on a spacesuit in the weightless condition, and later still we practised inside a mock-up of the re-entry craft.

If until this point I had had any remaining doubts about whether I wanted to go into space, the weightless training dispelled the last of them. In fact, I could hardly wait to begin.

Amongst the most physically arduous training we went through was learning the emergency procedures. An emergency in a space mission falls into one of two clearly defined categories:

there is the sort you can do something about and there is the sort you cannot. If the last stage of the launch rocket blows up a hundred miles above the Earth's surface, there's nothing you can do to save your own life and it is pointless being trained to try. Similarly, if a large meteor collides with the space station, that's it. Space travel has particular hazards associated with it.

Flight systems, however, are designed around precautions, safety measures and back-up arrangements. At most points in the rocket flight, and while you are in the space station, there are standard procedures for dealing with problems and emergencies.

Being struck by a small meteor, one that is large enough to puncture the hull of the space station but not to destroy the whole edifice, is something that counts as being a dangerous possibility (if not a probability), so we were trained to deal with it.

The key factor after a meteor strike would be the rate at which the station was losing air pressure. In all likelihood the hole would be small (most meteors are hardly larger than grains of dust) and the leak would therefore be slow. The instruments would probably detect the leak before the crew, so the first thing you would have to establish was exactly where the hole had appeared. The space station consists of a number of different modules, which can be isolated from each other by airtight hatches. You would act according to the area where the leak was found. A hole in the base block would present more of an immediate danger than one appearing in, say, one of the Soyuz craft docked to the station; in the long term, though, damage to the Soyuz (still needed by the crew for re-entry) would be much more serious if not detected and dealt with.

Tolya and Sergei's training included EVAs, which would include carrying out running repairs to the hull if it were damaged. Because my own time on the station was a relatively short one, I was not trained for this.

Nor was I trained to deal with a catastrophic failure of the rocket in the first stages of the launch, because no one in the crew is trained for this. The Soyuz craft has emergency escape rockets attached to the top, and in the early stages of the launch these will automatically fire (or can be fired manually by mission control) if something goes wrong. The rockets snatch the manned part away from trouble, then lift it to an altitude where the main parachutes can be safely deployed. This system has actually been used on one manned mission that suffered an emergency on the launch pad and the lives of the cosmonauts were saved.

This is not in itself something the crew can be trained for, but we were briefed on what sort of accident would call the emergency rockets into use and what would happen when they fired. (A lot of noise and shaking, extremely high g-forces, probable unconsciousness and a spell recovering in hospital.)

The real emergencies, which cannot only be anticipated but which fall outside ordinary simulator training, are in connection with the landing. If you have to make a hurried return to Earth, or if for some reason you land off course, there is a strong possibility you will end up in the sea and if you do it's likely for geographical reasons to be a long way from the Soviet Union. Less likely, you will end up in bushland, where the terrain or vegetation won't allow a helicopter to land and no one can come down from the helicopter to help you.

They trained us first for the bush landing, teaching us how to get into the chair that would be lowered from the helicopter. We practised this in northern Kazakhstan (where eventually I was to land, but not in an inaccessible area) and from here we moved to the Black Sea, where we advanced into the sea-landing emergency procedure.

There are two scenarios for a sea landing. The first assumes that the Soyuz re-entry craft is on fire and you have to get out in a hurry. Because the spacesuit is airtight it's also therefore watertight. There are inflatables aboard the Soyuz that you tie around your chests, then you get the hell out of the spacecraft!

The second scenario admits of a more unhurried departure.

This would come into play if the craft landed safely in the sea but in a remote area, the South Atlantic, say, or the Indian Ocean. Staying inside the Soyuz for a long period is not a realistic option: it's too cramped, it bobs around a lot, and it could easily fill with water. The crew therefore has to remove spacesuits, put on survival gear, collect emergency rations and equipment, then jump into the sea.

Simply stated, but the reality of all this is somewhat more physically trying.

The day we did the training was in June, and the outside temperature was about 30°C. Wearing our spacesuits and helmets, we climbed aboard the Soyuz mock-up on board the control ship and were then lowered into the sea. A flotation collar kept us afloat and teams of frogmen surrounded us in dinghies. (In a real emergency there would of course be no frogmen on hand and the flotation collar would be replaced by an inflatable 'balloon', which self-inflates in the hole from which the landing parachute is deployed.) With the hatch closed, we were then left to release ourselves.

The situation can probably be easily imagined: three space-suited adults in a cramped capsule, bobbing around in the sea, struggling in high temperatures to remove one complicated garment and replace it with another. In fact, the survival suit was not one garment but several: over the long underwear we were already wearing went a red polo-neck sweater, a sleeveless jumpsuit, a jacket, then duvet-style padded trousers and jacket, a pair of padded boots, a thermal hat, a rubber waterproof suit and finally a rubber hat on top of that.

It took us almost three hours to get out, but in the end we did so. My skin temperature went up 2°C during this time, and because of the wave motion there was a strong smell of vomit by the time we'd finished. This is an experience in which your relationship with the other people in the crew is tested to the limit. However, we made it.

Once in the sea you have to link up immediately with the

others, holding on to each other in either a line or a triangle, in case there's a storm. You have to be prepared to stay like this for up to three days.

All told, even though afterwards you know you can survive, you are left with the hope that the automatic landing systems will get you down where you wish to be: on the dry Kazakh plain, with a rescue helicopter only minutes away.

In December Tim Mace and I started crew training, which really marked the beginning of focused preparations for the flight itself. We began to spend an increasing amount of time in the Star City simulators, running through the many procedures so often that they became second nature. This kind of training is brilliant: during the flight itself almost nothing happened that surprised or scared me, so thorough were the preparations. We started the scientific training in February, working with the experiments organized by NPO Energia.

Both Tim and I knew, however, that the time was fast approaching when one of us would be selected for the prime crew, the other for the back-up. We had already been told that on 21 February we would be returning to Britain, where the final decision would be announced. Accordingly, on the Monday of that week, Peter Howard and one or two other Juno officials arrived in Star City. They had meetings with several senior cosmonauts and with the people who had been training us, presumably discussing which of us they thought should be selected. The next day, Peter Howard had separate interviews with us both, asking us how we felt about the training, the mission, what our feelings were about who should fly, why we felt this and so on. It was all a bit unnerving, but by this time, with so much of the training behind me, it had a less distracting effect. These months in Star City had made both of us much tougher, much more directed internally.

Tim and I flew back to Britain in separate aircraft; the Gulf

War was in progress and both flights were eerily empty. I was met at Heathrow by Peter Howard, then taken to a hotel in the West End. The imminent decision hung over us all like a cloud, reminding us of what had happened during the previous rounds of selection. Fortunately, this time, they did not drag it out. After some welcoming small-talk, Tim and I went up to our separate rooms. They came in to see us separately.

I was first. They told me I was to be in the prime crew. This would be subject to a medical examination in March and another immediately before the launch. They then went next door to see Tim.

I was delighted, but it took a few minutes before I could let myself believe that this wasn't just a weird dream. I knew that there were more medicals to get through and more exams to pass – but this meant that I was now likely to fly into space. I don't think I ever believed that it would be me, not until the day of the launch itself. I knew I'd worked hard, I knew I could do it, but then, so could Tim. Not expecting to be chosen, I had prepared myself for the disappointment of being told that I would be in the back-up crew. Now I thought about Tim. How had he taken his news, the news I thought would be mine?

Afterwards we all went downstairs, where a buffet had been laid on for us. Tim was amazingly good about the whole thing. We all knew there had been problems about crew selection before in Star City, where once the decision had been made about who would be flying and who would be back-up, the crews had not got on at all well together. I was therefore concerned about how this would affect Tim and me, but Tim immediately congratulated me, hugged me and seemed the same as he had always been. We stayed together through the meal, then had a couple of drinks together, but we were both exhausted. It had been about 10 p.m. when they told us the decision; 1 a.m. by Moscow time.

The next few days were filled with the now familiar, but no less tiring round of interviews, press conferences and TV appearances. Tim and I managed one quiet evening on our own together and the day before we were due to return to Star City I rented a car and dashed up to see my parents in Sheffield.

Back in Russia, training continued as before, but on 23 April 1991, at 10 a.m., Tim and I officially reached the end. We were declared ready to fly into space and were introduced to various luminaries from NPO Energia, who visited the training centre for the occasion. In the afternoon we were taken on an official tour of the Kremlin and the next day were conducted to what I now realized was the shrine of shrines, Yuri Gagarin's office. We signed the book of record, appending our own informal notes on what we felt about the prospect of going into space.

After this, a brief rest at the town of Ruza, and thence to Baikonur for the launch.

11

Landing

It was my last night on the station and I didn't want to go to sleep. I knew we were going to have to make an early start the next morning, so I came to the conclusion I might as well stay up. I decided to go into my bedroom, position myself by the window and stare down at the Earth all night, trying to capture it and remember it for ever.

We had been franking and signing the special space-station postal covers during the evening and it was slow if pleasant work, but by 1.30 a.m. we were finished. Musa went off to pack the remaining items in the re-entry capsule and to make sure it was stowed correctly so as not to affect the centre of gravity. Viktor and Tolya headed off to their sleeping bags, so the lights in the base block were dimmed. Sergei and I went down to the end of the Kvant 2 module (the part of the space station where the EVAs take place) and talked quietly about the Earth, about our families, our friends. Sergei knew what I was going to go through the next day and he had an idea how I was feeling that night, the night before landing.

While we spoke, the space station moved from daylight into darkness and it seemed as if the time had come to call it a day. I headed back into the base block towards my bedroom and floated past Tolya and Viktor, already asleep in their bags. In my tiny bedroom I wedged myself by the window; for a few minutes I watched the lights of the cities floating by below, but thoughts inevitably intruded.

I had had a fantastic time on board the station, doing experiments that were impossible on Earth, feeling weightless, watching our wondrous planet spin silently below. I had learned so much in Russia and made so many warm, sincere friends. Before that I had been able to do some interesting jobs, I had visited some marvellous places, I'd laughed, loved and cried. It's hard to believe that we will one day die, that this life, living, feeling alive, will cease to be. Even then, on my last night in space, I didn't believe I would die, but I accepted that I was ready, if it had to happen. I knew the next day was going to be the most risky day of my life. The landing was much more hazardous than the launch. All the crew knew that and we had trained for it, preparing for any conceivable problem with every action and precaution we could take.

It was not a frightening prospect and my thoughts were not morbid, or even sad. At that point I felt I had nothing to complain about, had left nothing unfinished. I had had a good time, I had done my bit, I felt I had experienced a lot and I was relaxed about it because I was ready.

After a few minutes of staring at the night side of Earth I began to feel cold. Staying up all night no longer seemed such a good idea, so I got into my sleeping bag. Because this was attached straight up and down against the wall it meant it was harder for me to see out of the window. I craned my neck for a bit, but I was pretty tired and even though I desperately wanted to stay awake I did drop off soon afterwards.

We were all woken by the alarm at 4 a.m. I had something to eat, but I didn't want to drink much because we'd be in spacesuits for several hours to come. In the Russian way we made haste slowly and eventually finished breakfast at about 5 a.m. After this we went down to the Soyuz craft for a last check, making absolutely sure everything was where we needed it to be.

Viktor and Musa put on some specially tight elasticated trousers, which by compressing their legs squeezed body fluids towards their heads. They had to wear these underneath their spacesuits throughout the landing, to help prevent fainting when they landed. Because I had been in space for only eight days I had no need to take this precaution. My one special preparation was to put on the band around my chest, so that mission control could monitor my breathing and heart-rate; apart from this, I left the station wearing what I had been wearing all week.

Sergei had a quiet chat with Viktor and Musa. Not only was it Viktor's first landing, it was six months since he and Musa had finished training. In this respect, I was a relatively important figure in the landing, since I was the most recently trained of the three of us.

I did not have much to do in this period. I made sure I had given Musa everything I wanted to bring back, in particular the photographs I had taken. I knew that because the scientific, practical side of my mission was based on Soviet experiments, if my photographs went back to Earth in an official container they would go straight to mission control and I would never see them again. So I made sure that all of them had been placed in the pockets of my spacesuit.

Leonov's chiffon dream-garment, though, stayed behind on the space station. As a bit of a joke it was fine, but it wasn't the sort of joke that would survive much retelling. I was happy to leave it behind. One or two of the other things I left on Mir meant more to me: for instance, my Swiss Army knife, which Tolya had found so useful, and a tape of various music tracks that I had put together for him and Sergei.

On the whole I simply did not want to leave. I had been in space for only eight days (two of which were spent in the Soyuz craft) and I felt I had only just arrived. Eight days aren't long enough to make you miss your old Earthbound life, or even friends and family. I believe three months is probably an ideal,

optimum period: long enough to become completely acclimatized to life in space and to get some long-term work projects
completed, and also long enough to give a keen edge of
anticipation to the idea of going home.

We had discussed semi-seriously the possibility of my staying
on Mir a bit longer. The others all knew I was enjoying it. Tolya
and Sergei were themselves settling in, so they knew what it felt
like for me, while as far as Viktor and Musa were concerned after
six months in space another two days would not make a scrap of
difference. We tried to work out ways we could tell mission
control that we needed to stay a little longer. Tolya and Sergei
said, 'We'll pretend that we're not yet ready to take over the
space station, that we need a couple more days.' Of course, we
all knew that mission control would be completely unimpressed
by such an argument.

The time I had been dreading came at about 6 a.m., when we
started to say our goodbyes. As with all farewells, there was so
much to say with no words with which to say it, and for me it
was a real and wrenching departure. Tolya and Sergei were,
quite simply, the closest and most important friends I had ever
had, and leaving them in the space station was the hardest thing I
had to do in my life. Quite apart from what might be about to
happen to me in the next few hours, I knew that they were not
likely to return to Earth for at least another five months and that
they too had to face the same dangers when returning.*

We went through our farewells again for the sake of the TV
cameras, and then it really was time to go, floating for the last
time through the Kvant 1 module and into the orbital module of
Soyuz TM-11. I was to return in the Soyuz craft that had

---

* Tolya returned safely at the end of his planned five months in space, but Sergei
was requested to stay on for a longer period. He became known as 'the last Soviet
citizen', the object of some curiosity in the media. He finally landed safely after 310
days in space, returning to a country that had not existed when we left.
   Tolya is still a cosmonaut in Star City; Sergei subsequently went to the USA,
where he has been training for a Shuttle mission with NASA.

brought Viktor, Musa and Toyohiro into space. (My personally moulded chair had been carried through from Soyuz TM-12 during my stay at the station.) We all made a final check to be sure that everything was correctly arranged and then we closed the Soyuz hatch. Sergei closed the hatch on the space station.

The gap between the two hatches is important, because only by testing this can you be sure that both hatches have sealed. The air in the gap is pumped up to a pressure higher than in either the Soyuz or the space station. Then you wait. If either side starts gaining air pressure, you know there's a leak. At the same time you can be sure, if the pressure in the gap remains constant, that no air is leaking to the outside.

Even though both hatches were closed we could still hear what was going on the other side. We could hear Tolya and Sergei moving around and if we raised our voices we could shout to each other, so we still felt in contact with them.

During re-entry the orbital module is jettisoned, so to a certain extent we were able to pack it with rubbish and other discarded material. It's not possible to put in too much, because the mass of the Soyuz would be increased and have an effect on the trajectory when the retro rockets are fired on the way down.

There were things to do in both parts of Soyuz, but as soon as possible I went down to the command capsule, put on my spacesuit and climbed into my seat. Even though it was made to measure, it was still extremely tricky in a state of weightlessness trying to strap myself into it. Everything, including myself and the straps, kept floating away. Musa and Viktor eventually followed me down and got into their suits. We did a pressure check on all three suits; fortunately they were fine first time.

At 9.13 a.m. we undocked from Mir. First the pressurized gap between the two hatches was evacuated, then the clamps that held both craft together were released. A spring connector is used to push the Soyuz away from the space station and after a few quiet clunks and bumps we drifted gently away.

There were still more than three hours to go before we started our descent. There were the usual immense checklists to work down, but in addition we had to take photographs of the outside of the space station. This turned out to be a time-consuming chore and for Musa, who was actually taking the photographs, a physically demanding one too. While Viktor manually steered the Soyuz over and around the space station (we had to photograph it from every angle), Musa had to wedge himself by the window to get the shots. The seats in the Soyuz are made to fit with the spacesuit helmet on and closed, but if you try and sit up with the helmet open it becomes uncomfortable. As Musa not only had to have his helmet open, but had to manipulate the camera wearing the thick gloves, it was not an easy thing to do.

Throughout all this we were talking to mission control as well as to Sergei and Tolya. Gradually, our manoeuvres were taking us further away from Mir and the radio signals between us were breaking up. At one point Sergei played us a few notes on the keyboard, but soon Tolya said, 'We can't hear you very well any more, so we'll put on some music now and say goodbye.' They played the Tanita Tikaram track from the tape I had given them: 'The World Outside Your Window', one of Tolya's favourites. That was my real last memory of them: I returned to Earth with a lump in my throat.

We were passing over South America at about 12.30 p.m. when we fired our retro rockets and began the descent. When the burn was complete we were again weightless, but no longer in permanent orbit. Now we were descending rapidly towards the Earth. I could see nothing through my window; just the blackness of space.

This was not a time for staring out of the window. It was not so much that we had a lot to do, because the automatic systems were fully working, but all the way down we had to watch the instruments, checking and checking that the spacecraft was behaving properly. We were working alone: we had been out of contact with Mir for some time and, as much of our re-entry path was over the South Atlantic, we were unable to speak to mission control.*

Shortly before we were due to enter the atmosphere, at 12.38, there was a bang and a shudder as the explosive bolts fired to separate the command capsule (now more correctly called the re-entry capsule) from the other two parts of the Soyuz.

Entering the atmosphere is not something that happens gradually, or in a smooth curve of events. The upper atmosphere is 'lumpy', with some parts of it thicker than others. This is where the automatic systems continually adjusted the attitude of the craft, so that it was always heading down at the correct angle and with the re-entry heat shield in front. From our point of view inside it did not feel as if we were travelling in any particular orientation relative to direction, until, that is, the craft started encountering the first parts of the atmosphere. Within five minutes of our detaching from the other parts of the Soyuz craft g-forces were building up gradually but perceptibly: 0.1 g, 0.2 g, just enough to make us aware of being in the seats, to give the impression of sitting down once more. As we began to sink back into the seats, we tightened the straps.

While I had been in space I had grown at least 2 cm, a normal increment for a person of my height, and one that the design of the seat had taken into account. I hadn't been able to fit my shape snugly into it before the g-forces started building up. Only as

---

* This is a significant difference between US and Soviet space programs. With their worldwide network of satellite and relay stations, the Americans can be in contact with mission control anywhere above the Earth's surface. Only during the period of maximum ionization in atmospheric re-entry are the astronauts out of contact. Soviet cosmonauts are usually only able to speak to mission control for periods of about twenty minutes, while they are over Russia or in contact with a relay satellite.

soon as I was under deceleration did I feel the shape of the seat around me, and the fit was tight! My shoulders were really pushed right up against the top.

As the craft moved into the denser parts of the atmosphere, the deceleration increased noticeably. Coming back to Earth was physically much harder for us than leaving it in a rocket had been. $4\frac{1}{2}$ g was the maximum we had to put up with, and although this was fairly low compared to the g-forces we had been put through in training (up to 8 g in the centrifuge), after a long period of weightlessness it was a considerable burden. It must have been much worse for Musa and Viktor than it was for me.

As the friction outside increases, so the particles of the upper atmosphere heat up. They become charged, ionized, and sometimes luminescent.

From inside the craft, what we could see was the apparent colour of space shifting away from black. As the spacecraft began to enter the atmosphere, and the plasma built up, the colour turned a deep brown, then a dull orange. As the luminescence increased it became quickly much lighter: orange, yellowy orange, yellow, then extremely bright, almost white. While this was going on, the outside of the spacecraft was reacting with the hot ionized particles and soot was created. Particles of soot coated all sides of the spacecraft, including the windows. Because of this, the brightest part of the plasma display was hidden from me; I could see only sudden extreme bursts of light and sometimes it seemed to me that there were fireballs racing past my window.

The plasma started to disappear when we had slowed down sufficiently and soon after this there was another jolt from outside. The window shield (a transparent outer layer) was jettisoned, and with it all the soot that had been blocking my view. I saw a brilliant blue sky!

A few seconds later the parachutes deployed: first three drogue chutes, one after the other, then the main chute, a vast white shroud, one thousand square metres in size! The first drogue cracked open violently, snatching at the Soyuz craft before it had fully centred itself above us. We swung dramatically from side to side four or five times, 40° or 50° in the space of about three seconds. Even though we had prepared for this in training I was surprised how extreme it was. Musa said none of his earlier flights had been as physically shaking. After this, the other drogues and the main chute opened with a certain amount of jolting, but nothing as violent.

The time was 12.49 p.m. Only six minutes had passed since we first entered the atmosphere and only eleven since we jettisoned the other parts of the Soyuz.

By itself the re-entry capsule weighs some three tonnes, so in spite of the immense size of the main parachute, the rate of descent is fast. Without any further provision, the landing would be vicious, probably causing serious injury to those inside. For this reason, about ten minutes before landing, compressed nitrogen is pumped into the base of the seats as a shock absorber. This lifted the seats by 10 cm, and raised me above the level of the window. I was pressed up close to the control panel, with only a minute gap between my knees and the panel itself.

Now we felt hemmed in and heavy and in general we were starting to get hot again and were feeling physically rather strange. It was not dizziness as such, but a weird sense of reorientation. Nothing felt quite as it had before. I could feel my internal organs shifting about, readjusting to having weight again. Even my brain felt heavy!

Fifteen metres from the ground a proximity signal lit, warning us to brace ourselves, and I told the other two. They acknowledged. A moment later (when the Soyuz was only a metre and a half above the ground) retro rockets fired for an instant, cushioning us against the final impact. Then we hit the ground.

It was a windy day and for most of the descent we had been

moving laterally, relative to the ground. This meant that on impact we instantly tipped over and bounced hard on the ground. As it happened we were facing 'forward' on the first impact, so the movement was to rotate us roughly forward, as if on to our faces.

We hit the ground again, then again, first on one side then the other, spinning and careering across the rocky ground. After the first bounce we were being thrown around so much that we lost all sense of direction or orientation; all we could do was stay braced and wait for the impacts to cease. I discovered a nasty truth about being strapped in to a space suit: you can be protected from most major jolts, but the one thing you can't do is strap your head inside the helmet. When we bounced forward my face hit the visor. The microphone was there in front of my chin, and my lips became much more intimately involved with this than intended! My only injury was some minor bruising to the face.

We came to a halt at last, and there was a moment or two of blessed relief. As I realized it was over, that the craft was not going to bounce again, one of the other two spoke (I don't know whether it was Viktor or Musa).

'Are you OK?' he said.

Twenty-five minutes had elapsed since we fired our engine over South America and now our journey ended with us suspended uncomfortably on our sides. Musa was lowest, his window pressed against the ground; I was highest, and daylight poured in behind me. I could see nothing, because of the helmet, and because the shock absorber was still pressing me close against the instrument panel. We groped awkwardly towards each other and briefly gripped hands, reassuring ourselves we were indeed all OK.

I was unable to see poor Musa. We had brought back so much stuff with us that we were not able to attach all of it down. We had had to hold some of it and in the series of crashing impacts we had all let go. Now it lay on top of Musa, a small mountain of checklists, flight books, personal souvenirs.

We didn't want the rescuers to find us in this state and anyway we couldn't leave everything on top of Musa. Viktor handed me the first thing he could get hold of, his emergency procedures book that he worked through. It almost slipped from my hand as I took hold of it: it felt about ten times heavier than I had imagined! Bit by bit, we moved the rest of the stuff from Musa, but it was tremendously hard work. It wasn't simply a case of having to lift objects that felt heavy, but our own bodies also felt incredibly weak and heavy. Just to move my arm was a major effort.

We knew the rescuers must be close at hand, because we had been in contact with them during the descent and they had been following us down, so it was only a matter of time before we were released. However, this was an uncomfortable time. It affected us all, because we were hanging sideways in our straps and suffering from the feeling of weight, but Musa was going through the worst of it. He always suffered from space sickness and, now we were back under the full effects of Earth's gravity, he was feeling nauseated, he was sweating and he said he was desperate for something to drink. Viktor and I shared the last two symptoms.

However, there were a few things we could do to make ourselves a bit more comfortable while waiting. We released the parachute as soon after landing as possible, which immediately stopped the capsule from moving around. We took off our gloves and opened our helmets and were able to turn off the ventilator. Normal air was now coming in from outside, through a valve that had opened automatically during the last stages of the descent.

Within five minutes of touching down, I was aware of a strobing effect in the light coming down through the window behind me and knew that a helicopter had arrived. Shortly afterwards, the hatch was opened and people began sticking their heads in and saying hello and shaking hands all round. The sweet smell of the *polin* wormwood grass drifted in. It was all extremely sociable and cheerful, but we were desperate to have the capsule righted.

We knew, we had been trained to know, that righting the capsule was not a quick or easy job. For one thing, the outer shell was still hot, so it was difficult for people to get too close or handle it to any great extent. Also, one side of the capsule was emitting radiation, part of its signalling process. Eventually, however, they did manage to get ropes around us and we were pulled upright.

It took them only about twenty minutes from landing to get Viktor out; he had to be first because he was in the central seat. Then they turned their attention to Musa, who was feeling worse than ever. They seemed concerned about him and worked quickly to lift him out. It was hard work for all involved, including Musa. He had to raise himself to a position where the people outside, who were lying down on top of the Soyuz craft and reaching in, could help him to move over to the middle. When they got a strong hold on him he was lifted through the hatch, while I shoved a bit from below.

My turn came about forty minutes after landing. The man working at the hatch told me that Tim had come along, and also Peter Howard. I passed out personal items to Tim for him to look after, then they got their arms down to me and dragged me up through the hatch. They sat me on the top of the capsule for a while and I waited there, catching my balance, feeling the sunshine on me, smelling the sweet grass. And all around, crowds of people! The Soyuz, now it was on the ground, seemed smaller than ever, not much taller than an average man, but it gave me a little bit of elevation above all the faces. While we had been waiting inside the Soyuz, a tent city had sprung up around our landing position. Generators roared in the background; helicopters stood by. Someone passed me up a huge bunch of red roses.

There was a little chute they had erected down the side of the spacecraft, made of padded material, and when everyone was sure I was ready, two guys on top held my shoulders and I slid down. The people at the bottom caught me. They helped me to my feet, supported me as I walked a few paces, then lowered me into one of the big chairs they had brought along. The doctors crowded round, checked my blood pressure and pulse and so on, just like the old days. I was being filmed and photographed; I could see reporters not far away.

Later, when the doctors had cleared us, we took off our spacesuits, had a drink and then, with great relief, I managed to get one of the nurses to bring me a pan I could use as a toilet. More medicals ensued, until at last they said we could go.

I was being supported as I moved around, my sense of balance having been affected so that I couldn't walk without falling over. After a while I could walk OK, but not in a straight line. I started out towards the helicopter to which I had been assigned, with someone on each side of me, but the further I went the more my coordination returned. By the time I reached the helicopter I was walking on my own.

Epilogue

Three days after the end of the mission I was back in Star City and officially confined to the doctors' 'hotel'. I was supposed to be under medical observation until I had recovered from the rigours of the flight. In fact, as everyone knew, I had felt all right within an hour or two of landing and two days later I was as fit as I had been before the launch. They could not let me go, however, until everyone was totally satisfied. After three days of tests I was confronted by one last doctor. He prodded and peered in the usual way, then sat back in his chair and looked at me appraisingly.

'You're fit,' he said. 'You know that, don't you?'

'Yes.'

'In fact, you're one hundred and fifty per cent fit, and you're unlikely to suffer from anything serious for the rest of your life.'

'Does this mean you're going to discharge me?' I said. I had to be back in Britain in a few days' time.

'Yes, you can go,' he said. 'But there is an exception to what I just said. You do have an illness that you will suffer from in future. I'm afraid it's incurable.' He closed his notepad. 'Cosmonauts never recover from it. It's a longing to go back.'

Index

Afanasyev, Viktor Mikhailovich
  greeting on Mir, 98–9
  landing preparations, 171, 172
  landing, 179
air pressure *see* pressure
Akiyama, Toyohiro, 39–40
Aldrin, Buzz, 44
antennae
  docking problems, 65
Antequera Ltd, 75, 84, 94, 110,
    122
  announce selection for training,
    126
  legal matters, 96, 119
  shortfall in sponsorship, 157–8
  dissolved, 158
Armstrong, Neil, 44
Artsebarski, Anatole Pavlovich
    (Tolya), 18, 172
  training, 153, 163
  launch, 21, 26, 40–3
  manual docking, 66–8
  farewell to, 172, 174
Artsebarski, Natasha, 21
astronauts/cosmonauts *see also*
    selection process
  basic requirements, 70
  psychological motives, 79–80,
    94
  requirements for, 49–51

training at Star City, 151–4,
    160–8

Baikonur Cosmodrome, 17, 20
  accommodation, 19
  Akiyama's launch, 39–40
  launch site, 22
Birkbeck College, 47, 69
Black Sea, 164
braslets, 21, 61, 62, 103
Britain
  view from space, 131, 133
British Embassy, Moscow, 123,
    154
British Interplanetary Society, 11,
    12
Brooks, Gordon, 125
  selection of four, 90, 91
  evaluation in Russia, 109–25
  back-up, 126–8
Brunel University, 75
BUPA
  medicals, 73–4

centrifuge, 85–6
  Star City, 116
  up to 8 g-forces, 176
ceramics, 149
Challenger, 38
Clarke, Arthur C., 11–13

Cleator, P. E., 11
clouds, 132
condensation
    inside capsule, 35
cosmonauts *see* astronauts/
        cosmonauts
crew training, 160, 166
crystals
    experiments in space, 149
    luminescent, 71

dangers
    docking, 66
    safety training, 162–6
Djanibekov, Major General,
        123
docking, 52, 98–9
    manually, 65–8
    window for, 58
Dodd, Joanna, 88, 120

Earth
    colour analysis, 150
    view of, 58, 107, 108, 130–6
electrical storms, 134–5
electrotopography, 107, 149–50
emergency procedures, 162–6
Energia, 109, 157, 158
Exhibition of Economic Achieve-
        ments, 117
experiments, 103, 108, 171
    advantage of space environment,
        145
    air samples, 147–8
    crystals, 149
    Earth colour analysis, 150
    electrotopography, 107,
        149–50
    lemon tree, 148
    medical, 147
    Prognos, 107, 147
    seeds and seedlings, 148, 149
    snails, 148
    Vita, 148

flying
    parachuting, 160–1
    weightlessness training,
        161–2
food
    appetite in space, 64
    drinking in space, 57
    first meal in space, 59
    Russian, 18–19, 111, 113
    variety on Mir, 104
forest fires, 133

g-forces
    centrifuge, 85–6
    launch, 41–3
    re-entry, 175–6
Gagarin, Yuri, 44
    heroic importance, 27–8
    traditions, 20, 26, 27–30
Glavkosmos (Soviet Space
        Administration), 75
Gorbachev, Mikhail, 101, 114
Graham, Peter, 84, 119, 120, 122,
        129, 158
Granard Rowland Communica-
        tions, 88, 90, 94, 120, 143
Gulf War, 135, 166–7
GUM, 124

Harrogate Ladies' College, 101,
        104
height
    increase in space, 175
Howard, Air Vice-Marshal Peter
    at landing, 180
    in Moscow, 111, 112
    selection process, 72, 77, 166

Institute of Aviation Medicine,
        Farnborough, 84–6
Ivanov, General-Colonel
        Vladimir, 26

Japanese astronauts, 39, 118

Jordanthorpe Comprehensive
    School, 46
Juno Space mission, 75, 122, 166

Kazakhstan, 17
    local well-wishers, 21–3
Kikuchi, Ryoko, 161, 162
Kremlin, 124
Krikalyev, Sergei Konstantino-
    vich, 18
    training, 163
    launch, 26, 32, 40–3
    experience, 66
    farewell to, 172, 174
Krivalapov, Dr Vladimir, 18
Kuwait, 135
Kvant module, 67, 99, 169

landing
    emergency training, 164–6
    preparations, 171
    descent, 174–8
    back on earth, 178–81
launch, 40–3
    Gagarin rituals, 26–30
    preparation, 35–40
    the rocket, 30–5, 41–3
Leninsk, 17
Leonov, Alexei Arkhipovich, 12,
    18, 171
    pre-launch rituals, 28–30
London University *see* Birkbeck
    College

Mace, Tim, 96
    evaluation in Russia, 109–25
    selected for training, 90, 91, 121,
    126–8
    exchange with Antequera, 129
    legal details, 137
    friendship during training, 154–5
    back-up, 18, 167–8
    present for landing, 180
magnetic field, 148

Manarov, Musa Khiromanovich
    greeting on Mir, 98–9
    landing preparations, 171, 172
    rough landing, 178–9, 180
Mars Confectionery, 47–8, 72,
    127
    supportive, 73, 78–9, 83, 86
    farewell, 95
McAuliffe, Christa, 38–9
media
    first experiences of, 74, 77–8
    potted descriptions of four, 92–3
    PR windup, 91–2
    selection TV appearance, 126–7
    deferring to, 141
medical exams, 72–4, 77, 79, 121
    ENT tests, 113
    post-flight, 181, 183
    pre-launch, 18–20, 23
    Russians in London, 87, 88
    vestibular tests, 116
MIK assembly area, 22
Mir, 17
    docking, 65–8
    first impressions, 99–103
    mock-up, 116
    orbit, 130
    orientation within, 59
    power loss, 105–6
    training, 159
    view of Earth from, 130–6
Moscow
    days at hospital, 109–15,
    118–20, 122
    transportation, 155–6
Moscow airport, 124–5
Moscow Narodny Bank, 75
    saves mission, 158
music, 37, 157

oxygen levels, 62–3

parachutes, 159–60
Prelude to Space (Clarke), 13

pressure
  between hatches, 173
  loss from meteor strike, 163
Prognos, 107, 147
psychological testing, 79–80, 113

quarantine, 17, 22–3

radio
  ham equipment, 101–2, 104, 108
rockets *see also* Soyuz; space
    vehicles
  in launch, 41
  layout of sections, 32, 34
orientation, 59
Royal Aeronautical Society, 77
Russian language, 50–1, 151–3,
    154, 159

safety training, 162–6
Science Museum, London, 125
sea landings, 164–4
seeds and seedlings, 148, 149
selection
  first steps, 72–5
  Brunel and RAeS, 76–7
  medical exams, 80–83
  psychological tests, 79–80, 82
  final four, 88–97
  down to two, 120–2, 125–9
  HS chosen for prime crew, 166–8
Sharman, Helen
  childhood and education, 44–9
  jobs, 46–8
  hears job announcement, 69–71
  applies to be astronaut, 70–2
  first stage of selection, 72–89
  selection down to four, 89–97
  evaluation in Russia, 109–25
  one of two selected, 125–9
  cosmonaut training, 151–4,
    160–8
  chosen prime crew, 166–8
  morning of launch, 17–26

prepares for launch, 26–40
  launch, 40–3
  flight to Mir, 52–68
  farewell to Mir, 169–74
  returns to Earth, 174–83
Sharman family, 92, 126, 128
  background, 45, 48
  launch farewell, 25–6, 38
Sheffield University, 46
sleeping, 60–62
Smith, Clive, 96
  selection of four, 90, 91
  evaluation in Russia, 109–25
  back-up, 126–8
snails, 148
solar panels, 58, 105, 136
Soviet Space Administration
    (Glavkosmos), 75
Soyuz, 17
  safety, 38–9, 163–4
  training, 159
  docking port, 67
  entering for launch, 30–5
  flight to Mir, 52–68
  return to Earth, 171–8
  on the ground, 180–1
Soyuz/Apollo mock-up, 117
Space Museum, Moscow, 117
spacecraft
  emergency training 162–6
  MIK assembly area, 22
spaceflight
  theory v practice, 57
  training, 160
spacesuits, 23–5
  cold feet, 36, 40
  comfort in space, 52–3
  pressure, 24–5
  training, 162, 164–5
spinning chair, 85, 116
sports training, 153–4
Sputnik I, 11, 117
Star City, 115–16
  accommodation, 153, 156–7

sports facilities, 153–4
training, 151–4, 160–8
stars
view from Mir, 134

talisman, 37, 40, 41
team spirit, 50
on Mir, 106
Tikaram, Tanita, 174
toilets, 56, 63–4
training *see* under astronauts/
cosmonauts

ventilation fans, 105

vestibular tests, 116
Vita, 148

water
drinking in space, 57
weightlessness
body fluids, 61–2
braslets, 21, 61, 62, 103
dust and sneezing, 147
first experience of, 53, 56
training, 153–4, 161–2
Wolff, Professor Heinz, 76–7
wormwood grass (*polin*), 29,
180

Also available from Victor Gollancz

How the World Was One
The turbulent history of
global communications

ARTHUR C. CLARKE

Arthur C. Clarke has been one of the most influential
commentators on – and prophets of – the communications technology which created the global village. Now,
drawing on his own experiences, including his famous
Wireless World article on 'extra-terrestrial Relays' which
predicted communication satellites, Clarke has produced
an enthralling history, charting the rivalry between
comsat and cable, and the setbacks and triumphs of the
technology that changed the world for ever.

'A vastly agreeable blend of history, science, thumb-
nail biography, reminiscence and – as one expects from
this renowned science fiction author – heady prophecy'
– *Wall Street Journal*

'Clarke has brought to bear all his formidable story-
telling skills to bring to life this story of disaster and
triumph' – *Manchester Evening News*

'A fascinating account of how we got *here* from *there*:
the laying of the undersea transatlantic cables, and its
frustrations have never been so well described' – *Daily
Telegraph*

ISBN 0 575 05546 4   £6.99 paperback

Odyssey
The Authorised Biography of
Arthur C. Clarke

NEIL McALEER
Foreword by Patrick Moore

From his early days on a Somerset farm, experimenting with crystal sets and refractor telescopes, Arthur C. Clarke was fascinated by science, both fact and fiction. This, his first biography, culled from hundreds of interviews with both Clarke and his family and friends, and with celebrities as diverse as Walter Cronkite and Carl Sagan, charts his extraordinary success in both fields.

Odyssey offers a unique chronicle of the man whose fiction, including his groundbreaking collaboration with Stanley Kubrick on the film *2001*, has received all of science fiction's highest awards, and whose visionary contribution to science has earned him the nickname Godfather of the Communications Satellite.

'Continuously fascinating. All the major elements of Clarke's life are described' – Charles Sheffield, *New Scientist*

'A worthy catalogue of Clarke's achievements' – *Daily Mail*

'Captures the spark of its subject's vision. Recommended' – *Critical Wave*

'A long overdue tribute' – *Manchester Evening News*

'A highly enjoyable account of the life and times of one of the great science fiction writers, pitched at exactly the right level for fans who want to know more about the great man' – John Gribbin, *TES*

ISBN 0 575 05573 1   £5.99 paperback